FACES OF AUSTRALIA SERIES

The Overlanders

The Faces of Australia Series consists of records and cassettes, together with companion books, giving a comprehensive and entertaining history of Australia and its people in musical and literary form. For details concerning the series write to:

Ted Egan, PO Box 1694 Alice Springs 5750, NT, Australia.

First published in 1984 by

Greenhouse Publications Pty Ltd
385-387 Bridge Rd
Richmond Victoria Australia

© Text, photographs and captions, Peter Forrest, 1984

© Songs and music where noted, Ted Egan, 1984

Designed by Rus Littleson
Typeset by Bandaid Productions, Melbourne
Printed and bound by Globe Press, Melbourne

ISBN   0 909104 74 3

The Overlanders
SONGBOOK

Compiled by Ted Egan
Text by Peter Forrest

GREENHOUSE PUBLICATIONS

Foreword by Dame Mary Durack.   Musical Notation by Erik Kowarski
Cover Illustration: Bill Gwydir on the Birdsville Track, by Robert Wettenhall, 1983

Text by Peter Forrest

Peter Forrest was brought up on a sheep station in central west Queensland. His father had spent some years 'on the roads' and many of Peter's earliest memories are of meeting drovers passing through with sheep and sometimes cattle.

In more recent years Peter has been vitally concerned with recording and preserving the history of outback Australia. He is well known in the inland for his writings, his radio and television broadcasts and for his practical involvement in the protection of places of significance to Australia's heritage.

Peter Forrest lives in Darwin.

Ted Egan

Ted Egan went to the Northern Territory of Australia at age seventeen, intending to spend three months in Darwin and then travel to South America to be a cowboy. Over thirty years later he still hasn't made it to South America. He now lives in Alice Springs and his principal interest is in collecting and recording the history of frontier Australia. He writes, sings and records his own songs, and regularly features these songs in the Ted Egan Outback Show in Alice Springs.

His early, and continuing contacts with Aboriginal people have given him a deep insight into their unique occupancy of this harsh, uncompromising yet starkly beautiful continent. He speaks two Aboriginal dialects, and has conducted Aboriginal Studies courses, mainly for urbanised Aboriginal children, at the Alice Springs High School.

His music is clearly influenced by his Aboriginal contacts and his Celtic ancestors, the first to come to Australia being a Cornishman to Portland, Victoria, in 1840. Despite the fact that the last Celt in his family was an Irish-born farmer named Peter Brennan who came to Australia over a hundred years ago Ted Egan's songs bear the unmistakeable stamp of the Celts.

Ted Egan is a graduate of the Australian National University, and gained his Bachelor of Arts Degree the hard way, studying under kerosene lamps in the bush. He majored in Australian Studies and Politics. He is in the process of producing a series of record albums, with companion books, titled *The Faces of Australia Series*. The series is Ted Egan's interpretation of Australian history, in song and verse.

5

Foreword

When I decided to undertake the mammoth task of producing a series of records and annotated songbooks to be titled *The Faces of Australia* I instinctively turned to Peter Forrest for advice and inspiration. In my opinion there is no better authority on the frontier Australia which has fascinated me all my life.

Peter Forrest was born in western Queensland of pioneering stock, and he is able to draw on real-life experiences of the many old bush identities he has met personally, and add to that the necessary academic disciplines required of the classical historian. When you hear Peter Forrest talk about the history of Australia you are sitting on the edge of your seat wanting more. This is real history, excitement based on the facts, not the dry, dull stuff that caused most of us to hate history studies at school. Peter Forrest whets the appetite. An insatiable researcher himself, he is the one who has provided inspiration for many like myself to reach the point where history books are read for enjoyment.

In the first album of the series, *The Overlanders*, Peter Forrest unstintingly passed on research material about legendary figures like Nat Buchanan and Harry Redford. He was the reason for my writing the song *The Drover's Boy*, a tribute to the many Aboriginal women who worked in droving teams and on pastoral properties in the early days. It is only natural that Peter should write the text for this, the first companion songbook in the series. I am sure the reader will be similarly inspired by Peter's text.

Ted Egan
Alice Springs, Australia, 1984.

Foreword to the Series

T ed Egan's plan to release a series of record albums with accompanying books is one that should have the enthusiastic support of his wide range of listeners.

The records and tapes he has already produced give a moving and multi-sided picture of the opening up of the vast inland of this continent. His songs are not only entertaining, they are also of considerable educational significance and arouse in all age groups an interest in, and an appreciation of, the men and women who pioneered our 'great Australian loneliness'. His repertoire is a subtle mingling of the romance, pathos and humour of our unique Australian heritage.

I have therefore, no hesitation in recommending wholeheartedly support for this project and I have every confidence that it will be of great popular appeal.

Mary Durack

MARY DURACK
PERTH

W.A. Newspapers

Acknowledgements

Our sincere thanks go to:

- Dame Mary Durack for her Foreword, her permission to print *Ben Hartigan* and for her generous support and inspiration at all times;
- Chris Buch for his permission to record and print *Johnny Stewart, Drover*;
- All the artists who helped in the recording of the album *The Overlanders* but particularly Nerys Evans, The Bushwackers, The Mucky Duck Bush Band and Bert Vickers;
- Eddie Hackman for his permission to reproduce his sculpture of Nat Buchanan;
- Robert Wettenhall for his cover illustration *Bill Gwydir on the Birdsville Track*;
- Yvonne Dorward, Jeanette Cook and Mark Egan for their illustrations;
- Erik Kowarski for his musical notation, and for the musical direction of the album;
- The following people who helped to provide the source material upon which the album and this book are based:

Bryan Bowman
Bill Brook
Chris Buch
Mona Byrnes
Harry Clark
Bill Coleman
Jeff Corfield
Jack Cotton
Cliff Donahue
Peter Donovan
Jack Dowler
Ted Fegan
Bill Forrest
Jack Forrest

'Boy' Forster
Ivy Fuller
Brian Gough
Dorothy Hall
Bob Hart
Les Haynard
Jean Hayes
Ted Hayes
George Hobson
Edna Zigenbine Jessop
Dick Law
Doug Lillecrap
Arch McGill
Mick Madigan

Robey Miller
Dr Tom Murphy
Howard Pearce
Sir Wallace Rae
Gordon Reid
'Darkie' Saunders
Dick Scobie
Doreen Smith
Jim Smith
Kelly Smith
Johnny Stewart
Margaret Voller
Hugh van Huytheysen
Bill Waudby
Milton Willick

TED EGAN
ALICE SPRINGS

PETER FORREST
(DARWIN)

Contents

Introduction

About a century ago Australia started to become one of the world's most urbanised countries — with the majority of its population congregating into cities along the coastline.

The great inland spaces of our country came to be called the 'Never Never' — a vast, fearful and little known area which was the domain of Australia's heroes. Into the Never Never went the last explorers, the miners, the settlers, the bush workers — and the overlanders. These were the men who (with a few women) ventured 'further out' into the real Australia. They lived lives which were to underwrite the Australian legend of courage, loyalty, mateship and incredible physical achievement. This legend was to become the spirit of the Australian nation.

This is a book about some of these people — the overlanders who took livestock across the face of Australia to establish stations on the pastoral frontier; and about those who later engaged in the profession of droving stock as a vital part of the pastoral industry. It is a book which focuses on the overlanding and droving of cattle to and from the huge stations in Australia's north and centre — because this was the setting for some of the longest and largest livestock movements in our history, and because this phase of history is still recent enough to be fresh in folk-lore and memories of living people.

Australia today seems to be entering a period of change which may well be even more dramatic than the transition of a century ago. There is a risk that the forces of change may obliterate the memory and record of the achievements of the heroic overlanding era. This book has been written in the hope that it will help, at least in a small way, to prevent that from happening.

The Overlanders

For twenty-five years after 1788, the first white Australians were hemmed into the coastal plains around Sydney by the seemingly impassable Blue Mountains and by official policies designed to confine the spread of the predominantly agricultural and convict settlement. Significantly, the first white explorers to find a way across the mountains were on a privately financed expedition and were more interested in grass than geography.

After 1813, the next seventy-five years of Australian history were to be largely the story of the rush for grass. The explorers continued to search for pastures capable of supporting fast growing mobs of sheep and cattle; would-be pastoralists anxiously awaited the news of the explorers' findings; overlanders pushed their mobs into the newly discovered country. The progress was not continuous, but overall it was surprisingly rapid. Despite the vastness of the continent and its often unfriendly geography, virtually all of Australia which is now occupied for pastoral purposes (and much of it that has been more recently abandoned) was claimed and at least nominally stocked by 1888 — the centenary of white settlement.

In the years before Federation and the first Anzac Day, Australians could refer to only limited national achievement, but no one could deny the record of human endeavour in the inland. Foremost, and uniquely Australian, were the overlanders.

Their movement across Australia was a series of advances and retreats. In the first years, exploration was slow. The MacArthurs and others were still evolving the fine woolled merino and were pioneering markets for its fleeces, while cattle numbers were limited by the small local market for meat. Until 1820, movement across the mountains towards Bathurst was gradual, but during the next decade Australia saw the first of the booms and busts by which its pastoral industries were to be distinguished.

Continued convict transportation and free settlement doubled the white Australian population to 70 000, so increasing the demand for meat. This and the opening of new wool markets in England fuelled a demand for land which pushed the limits of actual settlement well beyond the boundaries which had been officially defined to confine the spread until the land could be surveyed. Fatefully, the decade ended in drought and depression which forced a pause, even a retreat, in settlement expansion.

However, the setback was brief, and during the next decade, two new words came into use as men drove sheep and cattle to newly discovered localities. Squatters occupied the new grassy plains without any legal sanction, encouraged by a leap in the white Australian population to 190 000 by 1840, and financed by capital inflow from Britain. Overlanders took stock into these new districts and across long intervals of unknown country to the new decentralised settlements which were appearing on the coast.

The first of these new settlements was in what was to become the future Victoria. In 1834, the Henty family quietly crossed Bass Strait and squatted at Portland Bay, while in the following year, Batman and others also crossed from Van Diemen's Land (later Tasmania) to Port Phillip Bay. In 1836, British settlers came direct to where Adelaide now stands, to establish the 'free' colony of South Australia. Soon after, the Leslie brothers were pushing north from the New England district into the Darling Downs, and paving the way for pastoral expansion in the Moreton Bay hinterland when free settlement was permitted there from 1841. In the meantime, on the opposite side of the continent, an English settlement on the Swan River was struggling to survive.

All these new settlements had been established by using sea transport, either from the established settled areas of Australia, or directly from Britain. At first, sea transport was also used to import the livestock needed in the new places. But sea transport of stock was never satisfactory — losses were extremely high and those animals which survived took a long time to recover from the voyage.

Overland rather than sea transport was the obvious answer. But how could mobs be moved safely across the unknown country which separated the new settlements from the edges of established pastoral occupation? Men like Joseph Hawdon showed that it could be done. In 1836, with John Gardiner, he took cattle safely overland to Port Phillip. In 1838 he joined with Charles Bonney to be the first to take cattle overland to Adelaide. Edward John Eyre was not far behind — he was second with stock into both Port Phillip and Adelaide, then in 1839 searched vainly for a route from South Australia to the Swan River across the Nullarbor Plain. In 1840, Eyre took stock to Albany by sea, and then overland to Perth. Eyre gained fame as an explorer as well as overlander when he succeeded in crossing the Nullarbor in 1840. With men like Charles Sturt, William Landsborough, Nat Buchanan, Alexander Forrest, John McDouall Stuart and many others, Eyre's work demonstrated that very often the most successful of the Australian explorers were primarily motivated by the drive to find new pastoral land and stock routes to it.

What was the background of these men who established the Australian overlanding tradition? What were the personal resources of skill and experience which equipped them to respond to demand and opportunity? Answers to these questions can be discerned from the writings by and about these first overlanders. Clearly they were shrewd, tough, resourceful, with at least some formal education. The leaders of the early overlanding parties were almost all born outside Australia, and came here seeking opportunity for modest capital and much talent. However, we learn from Hawdon that the men employed as stockmen, cooks, horse tailers and general hands were very often Australian born, or perhaps ex-convicts. These men commonly had a lifetime of experience in the Australian bush.

Men like Hawdon and Eyre engaged in overlanding ventures on their own account or in partnership with investors prepared to back their speculative journeys. Later, overlanding work came to be taken over by contractors who had gained their experience with early overlanders, or on frontier stations. Some of them may have been Australians of long standing, but many others were migrants. The new settlers in what was to become Victoria were unable to bring their assigned convicts from Tasmania, and so they urged friends and relatives to come from Britain, or engaged agents to find prospective emigrants, particularly from Scotland.

The contribution and influence of these people of Scottish origin or descent to Australian overlanding has been so powerful that an explanation must be sought.

As early as 1359, two Scottish drovers were given safe conduct to bring cattle into England and, ten years later, the Scots Parliament imposed customs dues on cattle exported to England. By the early years of the sixteenth century, cattle were coming from the Western Isles and the Highlands toward the Lowlands and thence as far afield as London. The drover was already celebrated in song and verse — none more than Rob Roy, who was a drover and honest cattle dealer before living as an outlaw and cattle thief. Sir Walter Scott, the grandson of a drover, wrote 'The Highlanders, in particular, are masters of this difficult trade of droving, which seems to suit them as well as the trade of war. It affords exercise for all their habits of patient endurance and active exertion. They are required to know perfectly the drove roads which lie over the wildest tracts of country, and to avoid as much as possible the highways which distress the feet of the bullocks, and the turnpikes which annoy the spirit of the drover; whereas on the broad green or grey track which leads across the pathless moor, the herd not only moves at ease and without taxation but, if they mind their business, may pick up a mouthful of food by the way.'

Others describe the Scottish drovers as 'great stalwarts, shaggy and wild, their clothing and physique suited to the hardships of their lives'. Of necessity, they were heavily armed against cattle raiders and dressed usually in homespun tweeds, smelling of heather and peat smoke. A coarse plaid and a ram's horn filled with whisky had to suffice for warmth even on the coldest nights. The drover's food was a bag of oatmeal and a few onions, replenished every few days as opportunity offered.

A nineteenth century visitor compared favourably the skill and organising ability of a Scottish drover to that of the Duke of Wellington. 'To purchase a thousand cattle from a multitude of individuals and march them, in one or more great battalions, from the extremity of Scotland into the centre of England, at the expense of only a few shillings each, is an undertaking that requires genius, caution and provision for many contingent circumstances, beside the knowledge which is requisite to their disposal to such advantage as may encourage the continuance of the trade.'

These then were some of the skills and resources which came into this country with the emigrants. As the heyday of Australian overlanding approached, the imported experience and traditions were to be merged with those of the native born, to equip the overlanders to undertake a pastoral expansion of breathtaking scope.

The catalyst for this new wave of expansion was the discovery of gold in 1851. In ten years, Australia's white population rose from 405 000 to 1 168 000 and fat stock had to be brought from further and further afield to support the thriving goldfields. The great movement of livestock developed from as far north as the Darling Downs, southward to the Victorian goldfields, with

*'. . . as they took up each selection
They'd a constant predilection
To head in the right direction
Further out . . .'*

Chips Rafferty as he appeared in the film 'The Overlanders'

James Tyson teaching pupils like Sidney Kidman that fortunes could be made in overlanding cattle to mining centres, and in building up chains of properties to facilitate this.

Gold generated capital, and an outlet was found for it in the stocking of back country with sheep and cattle. The pastoral frontier pushed north and west to the Warrego district into inland Queensland, and toward Lake Eyre in South Australia. New country was opened up in the search for lost explorers Burke and Wills, and by a South Australian search for a route from south to north for a telegraph line and transcontinental railway. The actual connection of the Overland Telegraph Line to a cable linked with England in 1872 fuelled another inrush of capital, as British investors gained, for the first time, a means of rapid communication with Australia. The 1870s saw good seasons and good profits for both beef and wool, profits which were maximised by new techniques of property improvement, especially fencing and water supply.

By the end of the decade, all the factors needed to conquer Australia's last unsettled lands were in existence. The last explorers had glowingly described their new discoveries, pastoral investments had recently proved very profitable, good seasons had enabled flocks and herds to build up surplus numbers, government policy was achieving resumption for closer settlement in the old established districts, and above all, people of skill and daring were available to do the work.

These people were Australia's white nomads, who always wanted to be 'further out'. They were people with romantic visions of better country and hopes of founding pastoral empires for their children. They were physically tough, they were great organisers and leaders of men, and they were superb bushmen. They were 'The Overlanders'.

Further Out

Words & Music: Ted Egan

1. It's the ear-ly eight-een-eight-ies and a diff-'rent gen-er-a-tion has de-vel-oped, They're the peo-ple who are trav-'ling fur-ther out.__ They're most-ly Celt-ic stock, They're as sol-id as a rock, And they're un-de-terred by fi-re, flood and drought. Their ho-ri-zons are un-daunt-ed, Their cour-age will be flaunt-ed. As they take up each se-lec-tion, They're a con-stant pre-di-lec-tion, to head in the right di-rec-tion fur-ther out.

Chorus Fur-ther out we're the o-ver-land-ers rid-ing fur-ther out,__ We're un-de-terred by fi-re, flood or drought, As we take up each se-lec-tion, We've a con-stant pre-di-lec-tion, to head in the right di-rec-tion fur-ther out.

1. It's the early 1880s
   And a different generation has developed
   They're the people
   Who are travelling further out.
   They're mostly Celtic stock
   They're as solid as a rock
   And they're undeterred
   By fire flood and drought.

   Their horizons are undaunted
   Their courage will be flaunted
   As they take up each selection
   They've a constant predilection
   To head in the right direction
   Further out.

2. I am Patsy Durack
   I was born in County Galway
   I'm a man who's had a vision
   So we're going further out.
   My brother Stumpy went to Kimberley
   He travelled up by ship to see
   The floodout plains, the River Ord
   And the country further out.
   Our boys will overland our stock
   We'll each take up a block
   And though Nature's moods are meaner
   They say the grass is greener
   And the cleanskins' hides are cleaner
   Further out.

   CHORUS
   Further out, we're the Overlanders, riding
       further out
   We're undeterred by fire, flood and drought
   As we take up each selection
   We've a constant predilection
   To head in the right direction
   Further out.

3. I am Willy McDonald
   With my brothers Donald and Charlie
   And our cousin, Donald McKenzie
   We're travelling further out.
   We'll head for West Australia
   To the mighty FitzRoy River
   And we'll start ourselves an empire
   Further out.
   We'll take a thousand head of cattle
   With Nature we'll do battle
   We're forsaking all the towns
   We're off to Fossil Downs
   And our joy will know no bounds
   Further out.

   CHORUS
   Further out etc.

4. I am Phoebe Milner
   Droughted in at Cooper's Creek
   And we cannot take our cattle
   And our sheep further out.
   With my husband Ralph I'm trying
   To be first across Australia
   We've been seven years so far
   On the track further out.
   But we will get a big reward
   Of that we are assured
   We'll cross the OT Line
   Where we've heard the country's fine
   And the pleasure will be mine
   Further out.

CHORUS
Further out etc.

5. I am Kitty Gordon
   I married Nat Buchanan
   He's an overlanding man
   And we are travelling further out.
   With my brothers Hugh and Wattie
   And the Farquharsons and Cahills
   And Greenhide Sam
   We're riding further out.
   We'll follow Ludwig Leichhardt's track
   We're heading way out back
   Breeders to the Kimberley
   Another mob to VRD
   The only place to be
   Is further out.

   CHORUS
   Further out etc.

6. I am Alfred Giles
   I rode two thousand miles
   Taking cattle and some sheep
   To the miners further out
   Working on the OT Line.
   For Mr Todd that boss of mine
   I came to love the country
   That extended further out.
   And so I'm heading for the Katherine
   The river flats are really fine
   Work will be our recreation
   We'll set up Springvale Station
   We'll be the backbone of the nation
   Further out.

   CHORUS
   Further out etc.

7. Well Phoebe Milner's buried
   In the sandhills on the Cooper
   The Argyle Homestead's buried
   Beneath the Ord.
   The pioneers are gone
   And though their memory lingers on
   The people of today reap their reward.
   They were made of sterner stuff
   They never called 'enough'
   And as they took up each selection
   They'd a constant predilection
   To head in the right direction
   Further out.

   CHORUS
   Further out etc.

Further Out

'What sort of a father is it would hear of country like this for the taking and not be securing it for his boys? How could I expect them to settle down here, knowing of this pastoral paradise out west?' This was the reaction of Patsy Durack in early 1881 when he read the report of Alexander Forrest's 1879 expedition across the Kimberleys to the Overland Telegraph Line.

Within five years, the Durack clan was established on the Ord River after an epic overland journey from far south-west Queensland, so beautifully described by Patsy's granddaughter, Mary, in *Kings in Grass Castles*. Patsy Durack was a symbol for those restless Australians who yearned to be 'further out'.

He had come to New South Wales in 1853, aged nineteen, and was soon able to set himself up on a farm near Goulburn, the district which was the cradle of overland endeavour. Within ten years, Patsy and family were headed for greener pastures in Queensland, their imagination fired by William Landsborough's description of the grasslands of that colony. The Duracks, with close and distant family members, consolidated a huge aggregation of country on Cooper's Creek. Their prosperity seemed assured when Forrest's report arrived to tempt them into the wilderness yet again.

Patsy, with brother Michael, went to Perth to meet with Forrest, and was encouraged enough by him to organise an exploring party to assess the lands of the east Kimberleys in detail. By the end of July 1883, Patsy had started four mobs of cattle, totalling 7250 head, from the Cooper for the Kimberleys. Less than half survived the two year trip. In 1887, Patsy himself came to the Kimberleys, to find soon after that there were no significant markets for his family's cattle. The mining booms in the Kimberleys and the Territory had been short lived and had not developed a permanent population of any size, quarantine restrictions limited stock movement, agricultural development in the Territory had failed, and even Nat Buchanan, whose life we describe later, had been unable to find a market in Asia. Patsy died in 1898, financially ruined by a crash which broke his bank account but not his spirit. His family carried on, in partnership with the mercantile firm Connor and Doherty, and their fortunes improved with the opening of the Wyndham meatworks.

While Patsy Durack was on the Cooper, he may have learned of the arrival of Ralph and Phoebe Milner on the lower reaches of that stream. In 1864, Ralph Milner heard of a reward for the first successful overlander into the north of South Australia's Northern Territory. Milner determined to win the reward and set off with a small mob of cattle and sheep, heading for the Territory via the eastern side of Lake Eyre and then via far western Queensland. At Cooper's Creek, the party was 'droughted in', being unable to move forward or back, due to lack of water and grass. This fate commonly befell overlanders, but no others were held up for six years. Milner established a temporary station at Kilalpaninna, where his wife Phoebe died and was buried. In 1870, Milner returned to South Australia's settled districts to find that the Overland Telegraph Line was under construction. He determined to follow the Line north and so put together a plant of nine white men, three Aboriginal men and one woman, two bullock drays, one horse wagon, two spring carts, twelve months' provisions, material for the making of 50 pack saddles in case the wagons had to be abandoned, ten sheepdogs and fifteen greyhounds and staghounds. His stock comprised 7000 sheep and 300 horses. By early 1871, the party had left the settled districts of South Australia, and for the next 1200 kilometres they followed the track made by Overland Telegraph construction teams. Milner outstripped the construction teams at Central Mount Stuart, and from there to the

Roper River, he was guided by McDouall Stuart's journal. Just north of Central Mount Stuart, Milner lost 2000 sheep, due to their eating a poisonous shrub. This shrub was to cause losses to other overlanding parties until a safe detour around it was established by Alfred Giles. Then, at Attack Creek, where Stuart had been turned back by Warramunga warriors in 1860 and where later travellers were to encounter similar trouble, Ralph Milner's brother, John, was clubbed to death.

By December 1871, the party was approaching the Roper River. Provisions were exhausted and Christmas dinner comprised grilled mutton washed down with cold water. That day, they encountered Patterson, Superintendent Charles Todd's deputy on the Overland Telegraph Line. Patterson gave Milner the news that the Government reward had been cancelled, but he bought 2000 of the remaining 4000 sheep for two pounds, ten shillings per head — a generous price which reflected the desperate shortage of rations within the Telegraph construction camps. Milner spent the wet season at Red Lily Lagoon and finally Patterson purchased the balance of his stock. The trip may be taken to have ended when Patterson provided whisky for

Alfred Giles, one of the great overlanders

Milner and his men. Arthur Ashwin, one of Milner's men, wrote 'I think he (Patterson) nearly broke his heart when he saw his old Glenlivet whisky going in half tumblers. We were all pretty good on it after fifteen months' drought.'

The Scottish clan McDonald doubtless enjoyed a whisky too when their cattle arrived at Fossil Downs, in the Kimberleys, after a trip of more than three years from New South Wales. Donald McDonald had come to this country from the Isle of Skye, and like the Duracks, he had established himself and his family in the Goulburn district. He too wanted to be 'further out' and after corresponding with Alexander Forrest, he sent his son Dan to prospect the Kimberleys for country. Dan claimed country at the junction of the FitzRoy and Margaret Rivers, while at home, the McDonalds and their kinsmen the McKenzies joined forces to stock the new area. The McDonalds were to do the work, while the McKenzies put up the plant, equipment, stock and carry-on funds.

Donald McDonald was killed before the mob departed from Goulburn in March 1883. Charles and Willie McDonald set out with 670 cattle, thirty-two working bullocks, and eighty-six horses. They travelled via Blayney, Orange, Dubbo, Brewarrina and Charleville to Winton, where they arrived in mid-1884. Here they were held up for rain until September of that year, but they were then able to make for Cloncurry, Burketown and 'The Queensland Road', around the western shore of the Gulf of Carpentaria to the Roper River. Charlie McDonald became desperately ill and was taken from the Roper to Darwin and then by ship to Sydney. Willie, left with just two stockmen to help with the remaining 450 head, found that his supplies were all but exhausted. He left the cattle with his two men, telling them to hold the mob until he could obtain supplies from Wyndham. In Wyndham, Willie met his brother Dan, who had been in the Kimberley goldfields. They returned to the cattle and took the mob on to the Ord River.

Phoebe Milner's Grave, Cooper Creek SA

20

Willie now succumbed to fever and the mob was left with drover Joe Edmonds, again to be held until the McDonalds could go home to Goulburn, recuperate and return. For a time, Edmonds held the cattle aided only by a Chinese cook, but eventually he enlisted an Aboriginal guide and took the cattle on to Fossil Downs, arriving in July 1886. Three hundred and twenty-seven cattle were delivered. Charlie McDonald never recovered from the trip, but Willie was able to go to Fossil Downs. Eventually, his family reaped the reward for his perseverance.

Kitty Gordon did not enjoy the same good fortune. With her husband, Nat Buchanan, she spent a lifetime in the search for new land and stock routes, but their vision of good country securely held was never matched by their financial capacity to underwrite development costs or by the existence of markets for their cattle.

Their testament is written on the map of Australia: Bowen Downs, 'The Queensland Road', Glencoe, Wave Hill, Gordon Downs, the Murranji Track, Buchanan's Track. The place names extending 'further out' are their legacy.

Alfred Giles was born in South Australia, and already had a great deal of outback experience when he joined John Ross' exploring party in 1870. Giles assured Ross that he was 'sound in mind and limb' and had already learned to live on bandicoot and goanna. With three others, Giles and Ross set out on 8 July 1870, to explore the country along Stuart's track for water, grass and timber suitable for telegraph poles for the new Overland Telegraph Line. Giles came under the favourable notice of Charles Todd, the dynamic Superintendent of Magnetic Telegrams, who masterminded the Telegraph Line construction. When the line was completed, Todd commissioned Giles to overland 5000 sheep into the Territory and to progressively deliver portions of the mob to each of the telegraph stations between Charlotte Waters and Yam Creek. Giles gave delivery of the last of his sheep at Yam Creek and then rode south along the Telegraph Line to Adelaide. Late in 1874, he collected a second mob of sheep for the telegraph stations and again he headed north.

Through Todd's good offices, Giles met Doctor W.J. Browne, a wealthy South Australian pastoralist who was putting together mobs of cattle and sheep to stock his Northern Territory holdings, Springvale, Delamere and Newcastle Waters. By September 1877, Browne had organised the most costly and splendidly equipped expedition ever to enter the Territory. Twelve thousand sheep and 3000 cattle were entrusted to forty men, with Giles in charge of the sheep, under the overall direction of A.T. Woods, who also took charge of the cattle. Stores and equipment were sent ahead to Charlotte Waters and Alice Springs, while a well-sinking party proceeded in advance of the stock. In the sandy river beds of The Centre, water was bailed from shallow wells into tarpaulins laid in trenches, and the stock watered from these. Further north, the well sinkers dug a well on the north side of Bonney Creek, but rain fell before the stock reached the Creek, and the well was not used at this time. The cattle were divided into mobs of 500, each with a drover in charge, three stockmen and a cook. Each plant had a wagon to carry supplies, 25 gallon water tank and swags. The sheep were split into three mobs of 4000 and the whole operation was backed up by supply wagons pulled by horses and bullock teams. Giles and Woods were sworn in as Justices of the Peace before departure, so that they had authority to maintain law and order on the trip.

Giles records that the sheep were driven over a 105 mile dry stretch, ending at Anna's Reservoir, north of Alice Springs. For nine days and nights, the men with the sheep did not unroll their swags or wash. One hundred and fifty sheep were lost here, and a further 1000 through eating poison bush in the Davenport Ranges, despite Giles having scouted ahead for a safe detour. At Powell Creek, several men contracted fever, and were dosed with quinine. There was more fever near the headwaters of the Roper, and when the mobs finally arrived in the Katherine on 8 July 1879, 16 sick men were placed in a covered wagon and taken to a doctor at Yam Creek. Giles was left short-handed when even the healthy men began leaving to spend the big cheques which were coming to them. The stock was held by Chinese shepherds while Giles and Woods selected a homestead site twelve kilometres downstream from the telegraph station. By December 1879, a substantial stone homestead had been built and Giles was installed as manager of Springvale and supervisor of Doctor Browne's subsidiary stations, Delamere and Newcastle Waters.

This party was the only one to travel from South Australia to establish stations in the Territory's Top End. All the other original holdings of the north were stocked from Queensland. Regardless of the origin of their livestock, all of the Top End's stations (and almost all of those in Central Australia) were to fail within a few years. Springvale was typical. By 1887, Browne was forced to offer it for sale, but there were no takers. By default, Giles took it over, only to later abandon it.

Gordon Buchanan described the situation from first hand: 'Springvale was abandoned; and when in 1901 I rode through there, the old deserted homestead where travellers had so often received a cheery welcome, presented a dismal and forlorn spectacle. Indeed, on that trip from Victoria River to the Katherine, there was not a single settlement left. Willeroo, Delamere, and Price's Creek stations, because of the cattle-killing and other depredations by the blacks, had all been deserted. The only signs of former habitation were the gaunt and ant-eaten remains of the old houses, out-buildings and yards. Truly depressing sights in a new and fertile land.'

Giles battled on at Bonrook, closer to the local goldfield market at Pine Creek, and lived until 1931, appropriately venerated but with little tangible reward for his great pioneering endeavours. Thus his final years were typical of those who went 'further out'.

Springvale Homestead as it was in 1894.

Nat Buchanan was King

'First to stock the Queensland country which he and Landsborough had discovered, first with Crossthwaite's cattle on the Barkly Tableland, first with stock to the northern part of the Territory (Glencoe), first on the Victoria River, and now first on the Ord River, Nat Buchanan put up a droving and pioneering record which for its continental scope, has never been equalled in Australia.' So wrote Nat Buchanan's son Gordon in that wonderful chronicle of overlanding *Packhorse and Waterhole.*

The milestones of Buchanan's career speak for themselves. Of Scottish descent but born near Dublin in 1826, he came to Australia with his family as a small child. The family settled in the lower New England district of New South Wales, and by the time Nat came of age he was part-owner with his brothers of Bald Blair station. But the nomadic impulse in Buchanan's makeup was already strong, and in 1850 the brothers went to the Californian gold rushes leaving Bald Blair in the care of a manager. This was the turning point of Buchanan's life because he returned to find that during his absence the station had been so badly managed that it had to be surrendered to mortgagees. The rest of Buchanan's life was to be a search for new country on which he could establish a large scale pastoral enterprise for himself and his family. In the process, he opened up more new country than any other explorer or overlander in our history.

His first overlanding experience was gained in taking cattle to the new goldfields around Bendigo in Victoria. Then he was among the pioneers of the Burnett district behind Bundaberg in Queensland. There he met a kindred spirit in William Landsborough, with whom he explored the headwaters of the Thompson River in 1859 and again in 1860. Landsborough and Buchanan knew good country when they saw it, and they formed a syndicate to develop the station at first called the Landsborough Runs, but later renamed Bowen Downs. Late in 1861 Buchanan set out by sea from Sydney for the north Queensland port of Bowen. From there he blazed a track 500 kilometres overland to the new country and then set about pioneering it as the first manager of Bowen Downs.

Buchanan was joined on Bowen Downs in 1863 by an equally great pioneer — his bride Kitty, who was to be the first white woman in Queensland's central west and in many other places. The marriage, which appears to be have been idyllically happy despite much adversity, was for Nat to be the beginning of another lifelong association — with Kitty's brothers, the Gordons.

Bowen Downs might have re-established Buchanan on his own pastoral station but the cost of developing the huge enterprise was beyond the resources of the original syndicate. The Scottish-Australian Company based in Aberdeen was brought in to provide capital and within a few years the company owned the station outright. Buchanan was again on the roads.

The next ten years were variously spent droving and tin mining in north Queensland with a brief spell in northern New South Wales when Nat came perilously close to settling down on a banana plantation. Before long though he was again 'further out' — this time, in 1877, in charge of a mob of cattle to be overlanded to re-establish Rocklands Station straddling the Queensland-Northern Territory border near the future town of Camooweal.

From Rocklands, Buchanan must have seen the 'vision splendid' of millions of acres of unoccupied country in the Territory and adjacent Kimberleys. He was to spend the rest of his life trying to develop this last pastoral frontier and trying to find routes across land and water for its 'turnoff'.

The country lying between Rocklands and the Overland Telegraph Line was completely unexplored, so on 10 October 1877 Buchanan left Rocklands to remedy that. Taking with him only 'Greenhide Sam' Croker, Buchanan found good grass but no water on his trip to the Powell's Creek Telegraph Station. Buchanan concluded that large scale stock movement into Australia's Top End would have to be by way of Leichhardt's 1845 track around the western fringe of the Gulf of Carpentaria between Burketown and the Roper River.

Darcy Uhr had used this route as early as 1872 to take a small mob of cattle to the Territory goldfields, and this had been followed by one or two small mobs. However, it was to be Buchanan who would take the first big mob along this route and define it as 'The Queensland Road' to be travelled by over 200 000 head of cattle between 1878 and 1890.

Two Aramac pioneers, Travers and Gibson, had taken up country in the Territory — Glencoe, lying north of Pine Creek. In 1878 they engaged Buchanan to take the first 1200 head from Aramac to Glencoe. These cattle were to be the first to stock a pastoral station in the Top End.

Buchanan set out with his brothers-in-law, Hugh and Wattie Gordon, Travers, three other white men and two Aborigines. The plant included three drays (tracks cut through the scrub for the drays were to guide later overlanders), sixty draught and saddle horses, and food supplies of flour, salt, preserved potatoes, dried apples, lime juice, Epsom salts, quinine, together with leather, chains and rivets for saddle and harness repairs.

The route taken is worth tracing in some detail because (with one exception) it was to be the route for the movement of all stock taken into the Territory's Top End and into the Kimberleys for the establishment of the vast stations of that region. From Aramac Station the mob moved north-north west up Landsborough Creek and Walkers Creek to Marathon Station then on to the

Nat Buchanan
Sculpture in bronze by Eddie Hackman

24

Flinders River, the Albert River and then around the Gulf, crossing into the Territory at Settlement Creek to the McArthur River and then across to Leichhardt's Crossing on the Roper River, west along the Roper to the Telegraph Line, then north along the line to Katherine and then to Pine Creek and Glencoe. The total distance as the crow flies was 2000 kilometres but of course the men behind the cattle rode many times that distance. When travelling, the mob averaged sixteen kilometres per day but there were two long delays.

At the Limmen River Buchanan found that the country ahead had been burnt out and was uncrossable. The cattle were halted to wait for the first storms of the approaching wet season. Supplies were running low — the last had been obtained on the Flinders River and nothing had been got at Burketown as that town was temporarily deserted due to a malaria epidemic when the mob passed through. Buchanan took Wattie Gordon with him to ride on to the nearest store at Katherine for supplies. When the two returned to the Limmen River they found that Travers, when alone in the camp making damper, had been killed by Aborigines.

Rain fell and the mob was taken on to the Roper River, where a wet season camp was made. A number of calves were born on this camp and these were travelled on to Glencoe so that Buchanan eventually gave delivery of more cattle than with which he started.

During the trip, Buchanan's method was to himself scout ahead each day for grass, water and night and dinner camp sites. The horse tailer would bring the loose horses along Buchanan's tracks and the cattle would follow the horses. Buchanan arrived at Glencoe in March or April 1879. In 1880 he applied for leases over the area which was to become Wave Hill — the finest

On dinner camp with packhorses

country in the Territory's north. These leases were stocked in 1883 with 500 heifers brought over from Queensland by Tom Cahill, but in the meantime Buchanan had undertaken the largest long distance movement of cattle in Australia's history.

Following Travers' death, Glencoe had been purchased by the South Australian investors Fisher and Lyons as a base for a large pastoral empire they hoped to establish in the Top End. Buchanan was commissioned to bring 20 000 cattle from Queensland to Glencoe so that stocking conditions on Fisher and Lyons' immense claim could be met. Sixteen thousand head were started north from the St George district in south-west Queensland and on the Leichhardt River they were joined by 4000 head from north Queensland's Richmond district.

The cattle were split into ten mobs — each with seven men. The roll call of Buchanan's men included names that were later to be illustrious in the history of the north — the Gordons, Farquharson and Cahill brothers, Walby, Furnifull, Sayle, and Hedley — proving that Buchanan was as good a judge of men as he was of country.

Delivery was safely given at Glencoe early in 1882, and from Glencoe the huge mob was dispersed to other Fisher and Lyons' holdings including Victoria River Downs in 1883.

Having thus far been first with cattle at Bowen Downs, Rocklands and Glencoe, Buchanan was in 1883 to be first in the Kimberleys when he brought 4000 head from Queensland to Ord River Station for owners Osmand and Panton. Then Buchanan turned his attention to Wave Hill, and in 1886 pioneered the notoriously difficult Murranji Track between Newcastle Waters and Top Springs as a shorter route to Wave Hill than that via Katherine.

Cattle on Elsey Station, Northern Territory. Elsey, on the headwaters of the Roper River, was at the end of the 'Queensland Road'. Daily life on the station was recorded by Mrs Jeannie Gunn in We of the Never Never, *one of the most evocative and successful books about Australia ever published*

The explosion of capital and enthusiasm which had impelled Buchanan and others to race for Australia's last pastoral frontier was based on an illusion that profitable markets would quickly be found for the bounteous product of the new cattle country. Surely, the pioneers reasoned, the mining boom would bring population and a local market. Surely too, proximity to the millions of Asians would guarantee a market. These hopes then, as in more recent times, were doomed to disappointment, even though Buchanan's last years in the north were given over to a vigorous search for outlet routes and markets.

In 1890 Buchanan took cattle from Wyndham to Singapore by boat but this wasn't profitable and proved that at least for the moment the Asian market was neither large nor lucrative. In 1892 Buchanan returned to overlanding when he took cattle from Halls Creek to the Murchison goldfields, but this market wasn't large or secure enough for Wave Hill, Flora Valley and Gordon Downs — south Kimberley stations which Buchanan was then developing with his son Gordon and the Gordon brothers.

As at Bowen Downs 30 years before, Buchanan was over-extended. Development costs were met by the incurring of financial commitments which could only be discharged if profitable markets could be found — and they could not. In 1894 Wave Hill was taken over by Nat's brother Frank who held the station until it was bought by the English meat barons Vesteys in 1914. Nat again turned to mining and then managed Ord River Station. In 1896 (aged 70 years) he undertook his last exploring expedition in search of a direct route southwards from the Wave Hill area to the settled districts. He caused more than mild surprise when he arrived at the Tennant Creek Telegraph Station with a close description of the supposedly uncrossable Tanami Desert. But again there was no way out for cattle.

Buchanan left the Kimberleys in 1899 to spend the last two years of his life on a small farm near Tamworth.

His remarkable career is today little remembered except in bush legends in the districts which were once his. To the whites he was 'Old Bluey' because of his steel-blue-grey hair and beard; to the Aboriginals he was 'Paraway' because he was always going or had just come from 'far away'. He was remembered too for the green umbrella he sometimes used to protect his pale skin. He was a great organiser, leader and judge of men — the big trip to Glencoe proved that. He was of wiry build, stood about 173 centimetres and was extraordinarily tough and disciplined — he would often just rinse his mouth with water when others drank deeply. He was the greatest of them all.

King Paraway

Words & Music: Ted Egan

1. In the eight-ies Aus-tra-lia saw move-ments of cat-tle, In the world's dri-est con-ti-nent the dro-vers did bat-tle, With na-ture and thou-sands of hard miles were spanned, As two hun-dred-thou-sand were walked o-ver land, In-to Queens-land, the Ter-ri-t'ry and the Kim-ber-ley runs, In the fore-front was one of the lands fin-est sons, There are hun-dreds of dro-vers of whom we could sing, But ev-'ry-one knows Nat Bu-chan-an was King.____

Chorus Nat Bu-chan-an, old Blu-ey, old Par-a-way.____

2. What would you think if you came____ back to-day,____ It's not as ro-man-tic as in your time, old Nat, Not man-y dro-vers, and we're sad a-bout that. Fenc-es and

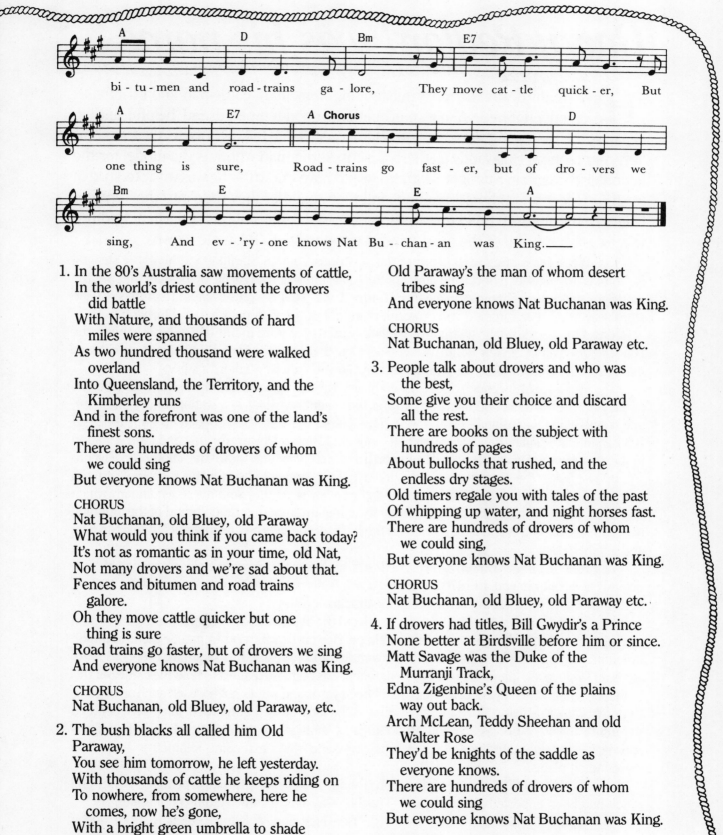

bi-tu-men and road-trains ga-lore, They move cat-tle quick-er, But

one thing is sure, Road-trains go fast-er, but of dro-vers we

sing, And ev-'ry-one knows Nat Bu-chan-an was King.____

1. In the 80's Australia saw movements of cattle,
   In the world's driest continent the drovers
       did battle
   With Nature, and thousands of hard
       miles were spanned
   As two hundred thousand were walked
       overland
   Into Queensland, the Territory, and the
       Kimberley runs
   And in the forefront was one of the land's
       finest sons.
   There are hundreds of drovers of whom
       we could sing
   But everyone knows Nat Buchanan was King.

   CHORUS
   Nat Buchanan, old Bluey, old Paraway
   What would you think if you came back today?
   It's not as romantic as in your time, old Nat,
   Not many drovers and we're sad about that.
   Fences and bitumen and road trains
       galore.
   Oh they move cattle quicker but one
       thing is sure
   Road trains go faster, but of drovers we sing
   And everyone knows Nat Buchanan was King.

   CHORUS
   Nat Buchanan, old Bluey, old Paraway, etc.

2. The bush blacks all called him Old
       Paraway,
   You see him tomorrow, he left yesterday.
   With thousands of cattle he keeps riding on
   To nowhere, from somewhere, here he
       comes, now he's gone,
   With a bright green umbrella to shade
       the fierce sun.
   On the Murranji, on the Murchison, on
       another new run,

Old Paraway's the man of whom desert
       tribes sing
And everyone knows Nat Buchanan was King.

CHORUS
Nat Buchanan, old Bluey, old Paraway etc.

3. People talk about drovers and who was
       the best,
   Some give you their choice and discard
       all the rest.
   There are books on the subject with
       hundreds of pages
   About bullocks that rushed, and the
       endless dry stages.
   Old timers regale you with tales of the past
   Of whipping up water, and night horses fast.
   There are hundreds of drovers of whom
       we could sing,
   But everyone knows Nat Buchanan was King.

   CHORUS
   Nat Buchanan, old Bluey, old Paraway etc.

4. If drovers had titles, Bill Gwydir's a Prince
   None better at Birdsville before him or since.
   Matt Savage was the Duke of the
       Murranji Track,
   Edna Zigenbine's Queen of the plains
       way out back.
   Arch McLean, Teddy Sheehan and old
       Walter Rose
   They'd be knights of the saddle as
       everyone knows.
   There are hundreds of drovers of whom
       we could sing
   But everyone knows Nat Buchanan was King.

   CHORUS
   Nat Buchanan, old Bluey, old Paraway etc.

Harry Redford was his name

'Harry Redford was the most outstanding horseman, cattleman and bushman I ever encountered. A big man, patient, good-tempered and helpful and so capable, the Kelly gang would not even have qualified to tail his horses.' That was how Territory pioneer Bullwaddy Bathern described the man who was the model for the fictionalised Captain Starlight. Bathern would have known — he was with Redford in western Queensland, horsebreaking, and then together they rode into the Territory where Bathern was to build up two very successful cattle stations and where Redford was to establish one of the most famous stations of all, Brunette Downs.

While most of us have heard of the illustrious Captain Starlight and his cattle stealing exploits as dramatised in novel and film, how few of us know of the real life of the man who was the model for the central character in *Robbery Under Arms*. That is a pity, because Redford's real life story is even more fascinating and powerful than that of the fictional Captain Starlight.

Redford (or 'Readford' an alternative spelling or alias) was born in the 1840s — probably in the Hawkesbury district of New South Wales. Some say that he came from England as a remittance man, but this appears to be yet another attempt to romanticise Redford's story.

We don't know much about his early life, but it is certain that in the late 1860s he was already on the 'furthest out' limits of pastoral settlement, working as a stationhand, contractor, and teamster in Queensland's central west. This district was just being opened up — in 1862 Nat Buchanan and William Landsborough had pioneered Bowen Downs, the first and largest station in the area. Bowen Downs stretched from north and west of Aramac down the Thompson River to a point just below the present town of Longreach. Development costs for this vast area were too much for Landsborough and Buchanan, and after a few years they sold out to a company which had its capital base in Scotland. Significantly the company kept the station brand of the founding partners — LC5 — a brand later carried on the hides of so many bovine migrants to the Top End and Kimberleys.

Redford knew Bowen Downs well and he knew that it wasn't closely managed, particularly at its bottom end. In 1870 he formed a grand plan which was to lead to one of the biggest, best known and most daring cattle thefts in Australia's history.

Taking advantage of a very wet season and the absence of any supervision by the station management, Redford began to muster cattle on Bowen Downs, and to gather them in a mob which he held on the plains near the later town site of Longreach. It is said that a very old set of yards on Nogo, a few kilometres west of Longreach, was built by Redford to hold the cattle but this is unlikely. Surely this superb cattleman didn't need yards and would not have left such an obvious clue to his illegal activity. Much more plausible is the local story that he used 'jump-ups' between the future towns of Longreach and Muttaburra as vantage points to get early warning of any approach. Certainly these residual outcrops command views extending kilometres across the surrounding plains.

By March 1870 Redford had mustered about 1000 head, including a pedigreed white bull which had been imported from England. This bull was almost to be Redford's undoing.

With only two accomplices, George Dewdney and William Rooke, Redford began droving the stolen mob down the Thompson, along Cooper's Creek past Burke and Wills' camps of only nine years before and then down what was to become the Strzelecki Track. By June 1870 Redford's mob had reached the northern limits of South Australian pastoral settlement.

The ruins of Harry Redford's hut on the banks of Corella Creek, Brunette Downs NT

Provisions were running low and Redford exchanged the white bull and two cows for provisions at the first store he encountered. Moving on, Redford sold the rest of the mob at Blanchewater Station for five thousand pounds — a handsome price. Redford, Dewdney and Rooke then went on to Adelaide.

In the meantime though, the 1870 mustering season had begun on Bowen Downs and by May the 1000 head were missed and the tracks of a large mob heading down the Thompson had been seen. Redford was quickly connected with the circumstances, and Butler, the Bowen Downs overseer, was sent to follow the tracks.

Butler made good time and was only a month behind Redford when he found the white bull. Shortly the rest of the mob was located and a hue and cry was started for the thieves. Redford was by this time lying low in western New South Wales but he was finally arrested in January 1872. Dewdney and Rooke were last seen in Melbourne at the end of 1871 but were never apprehended.

Redford was held in custody until his trial began on 11 February 1873 but he walked away from the Roma courthouse that evening a free man. The Crown had presented a cast-iron case, but the Roma jury was perhaps more impressed by Redford's daring and bushmanship than by sympathy for the absentee landlord owners of the stolen cattle.

31

In 1875 Redford was again in court at Roma on two horse stealing charges. Again he was acquitted but his luck ran out in 1877 when he was convicted of stealing a horse near Toowoomba and sentenced to eighteen months hard labour.

After his release in December 1878 Redford went droving around the booming mining districts of north Queensland. In 1883 he drove the first mob of cattle to Brunette Downs and managed that station until 1886. Then he established his own run, Corella Creek near Brunette Downs. This was not a success and within a few years Redford had surrendered his country to Brunette and had gone north to work on McArthur River Station near Borroloola. Redford returned to Brunette in the late '90s and lived as a pensioner at the main homestead or at his former hut on Corella Creek.

Although a gravestone first erected at Corella Creek but now kept at Brunette Downs homestead gives the date of Redford's death as 1906, the actual date of Redford's death is almost certainly 1901. On 12 April that year the *Northern Territory Times and Gazette* reported: 'News has been received by wire of the death by drowning, in the McArthur River district, of a well-known N.T. identity named Redford. Deceased visited Palmerston on several occasions some years ago in

Starlight's Lookout, once part of Bowen Downs — Central West Queensland

charge of cattle. No details are to hand beyond the fact that Redford was drowned on Corella Downs Station, and that the body was subsequently recovered.'

There was no inquest into the death and there are conflicting local stories. The best version seems to be that in early 1901 Redford set out toward Tennant Creek to look for new grazing country. Not long after leaving the Brunette homestead, he was drowned while trying to swim Corella Creek, which was in high flood.

Long before this *Robbery Under Arms* had been written by a Dubbo magistrate and frustrated squatter named Browne, using the pen-name Rolfe Boldrewood. Browne's imagination had been fired by court reports of the Redford case and his fictionalised story was first published in serial form in 1881.

The novel *Robbery Under Arms* has now sold over a million copies, and made Captain Starlight an Australian hero overnight. It was one of the first books read by the young Henry Lawson, and it was an important part of the new wave of Australian literature.

But the real Harry Redford was almost forgotten — a fate which unjustly befell so many of the pioneers of Australia's stock routes and stations.

The Mitchell Grass Plains of the inland were the setting for some of the world's longest movings of livestock as Australia's pastoral frontier moved north and west

Captain Starlight

Words & Music: Ted Egan

1. Out on the Bark - ly Ta - ble - land, __ not far from Bru - nette Downs, is the

grave of Har - ry Red - ford near the creek where he was drowned, Re -

spect - ed Ter - ri - t'ry Cat - tle - man, __ out - back pi - o - neer, __ But

not too man - y know a - bout __ his ex - ploits do you hear, __ So I'll

tell you a - bout his young - er days, __ a fas - ci - nat - ing tale, you know. __

Stole a thou - sand head of cat - tle and he walked them a - cross Aus - tra - lia, So I

want you all __ to raise your glass - es, drink a toast with me,

Har - ry Red - ford, Cap - tain Star - light, one, two, three.

Chorus

Cap - tain Star - light was his name, duff - ing cat - tle was his game, That's how

he a - chieved his fame, Cap - tain Star - light was his name.

34

1. Out on the Barkly Tableland
Not far from Brunette Downs
Is the grave of Harry Redford
Near the creek where he was drowned.
Respected Territory cattleman, outback
    pioneer
But not too many know about his
    exploits, d'you hear?
So I'll tell you about his younger days
Fascinating tale you know
Stole a thousand head of cattle
Walked 'em across Australia so
I want you all to raise a glass
And sing this song with me
Harry Redford, Captain Starlight, one,
    two, three.

CHORUS
Captain Starlight was his name
Duffing cattle was his game
That's how he achieved his fame
Captain Starlight was his name.

2. On Bowen Downs in Central Queensland
Harry carefully chose
A thousand head of cattle
Right beneath the squatter's nose.
He'd walk them down the Cooper
Where Burke and Wills had died
He'd cross the Stony Desert
No other man had tried.
But he made one fundamental error
Stole a big white bull you know
Thought it would be useful
To keep the cows content, and so
Down the Barcoo, down the Cooper
Down Strzelecki Creek
Into South Australia his fortune there
    to seek.

CHORUS
Captain Starlight was his name etc.

3. Harry sold the cattle, sailed for Sydney
Headed for the bush and there
He heard that all the Queensland cops
Were looking for him everywhere.
The overseer from Bowen Downs
Had followed Harry's track
Down the Cooper, through the Desert,
Through the great Outback.
And he'd found the big white bull
With the LC brand upon its rump you
    know.
So the bull was shipped to Brisbane
And railed on out to Roma, so
'The Queen against H. Redford'
became a legal battle:
'Harry Redford, you're under arrest,
You're charged with duffing cattle.'

CHORUS
Captain Starlight was his name etc.

4. The bull was brought before the Court
The Case seemed cut and dried
The jury was convened
So Harry Redford could be tried.
The jurymen were not impressed
With all the legal facts
But they did admire the bushman
Who'd performed such daring acts.
And, despite the Court's instructions
The jury said 'Not Guilty'. So
When you hear of Captain Starlight
There's one thing that you all must know.
If you've read *Robbery Under Arms*,
If you haven't, take a look,
And you'll find that Harry Redford
Was the hero in the book.

CHORUS
Captain Starlight was his name, etc.

Henry Lawson, Australia's great bush balladeer, by Mark Egan

Song for the Battler

Debate will always rage about the respective merits of the work of Henry Lawson and Banjo Paterson but there can be no argument that their literature made the outback the focus of Australian tradition.

At a time when Australia was on its way to becoming one of the world's most urbanised countries, these two men expressed in prose and poem what it was that was distinctive about this country. Lawson and Paterson were poles apart in many ways but they were united in the view that the people and places of the bush were uniquely Australian — that the geography and experience of the bush best expressed what Australia was all about.

Lawson, Paterson and their colleagues struck a chord of new nationalism which underlay the creation of modern Australia in the 1890s. This was the decade of industrial upheaval, of the formation of longstanding political alignments, and of the move to Federation. It was also the decade when the conquering of Australia's inland passed from reality into legend.

Through all of this these writers saw a brotherhood of the bush. To Paterson this brotherhood was in the sharing of the joys of the bush — the pleasures that the townsfolk never knew. To Lawson it was a brotherhood of social responsibility — a concern for the underdog. Paterson's vision was the broader one and perhaps therefore the more popular. Everyone in both bush and city could identify with Clancy and the *Man from Snowy River*.

Lawson wrote of, and for, a narrower group — the disadvantaged and oppressed. He believed that for these people a better life would come through republican socialism, human grace and dignity, and compassion in life's darker moments. Lawson's fundamental theme was to be best expressed in his prose, but the publication of *Andy's Gone with Cattle* in 1888 gave a clear hint of things to come.

Lawson was only twenty when he wrote 'Andy' (Paterson was twenty-five when 'Clancy' was first published in 1889) but he was the veteran of a deprived childhood in the bush. Lawson knew that every drover on the road had an anxious family at home and that droving trips were not just a pleasant excursion but were, for many selectors, the only means of earning the cash needed to make a go of 'starvation' blocks. He knew that for the 'battler' the bush was not at all like Paterson's vision from the verandah of 'Government House'.

Lawson died in 1922 after a life wracked by domestic turmoil and poor health. He suffered the disappointments of lack of appreciation and the dashing of his hopes for an egalitarian Australia. Paterson on the other hand lived until 1941, having achieved not only critical and financial success, but comfort in a world which he saw no need to change. The life and work of each man reflected different sides of the new Australian coin.

A century later their works are still the most powerful expression we have of the hopes, joys and fears of the people of the bush.

Andy's Gone with Cattle

*Words: Henry Lawson. **Music:** John Manifold*

1. Andy's gone to battle now
   With drought, the red marauder*:
   Andy's gone with cattle now
   Across the Queensland border.
   He's left us in dejection now;
   Our hearts with him are roving.
   It's tough on our selection now,
   Since Andy went a-droving.

2. Who now shall wear the cheerful face
   In times when things are slackest?
   And who shall whistle around the place
   When Fortune frowns her blackest?
   Who shall cheek the squatter now
   When he comes 'round us snarling?
   His tongue is growing hotter now
   Since Andy crossed the Darling.

3. The gates are out of order now,
   In storms the riders rattle;
   And far across the border now
   Our Andy's gone with cattle.
   Aunty's looking thin and white;
   And Uncle's cross with worry;
   And poor old Blucher howls all night
   Since Andy left Macquarie.

4. May the showers in torrents fall,
   And all the tanks run over;
   May the grass grow green and tall
   In pathways of the drover;
   May good angels bring the rain
   On desert patches sandy;
   And when the summer comes again
   God grant 'twill bring us Andy.

* These are the original Henry Lawson words. The
version often taught in schools:
   Andy's gone with cattle now
   Our hearts are out of order . . .
is the result of the unauthorised editing of David
McKee Wright, editor of the *Bulletin*.

The Drover's Life

There are many parodies of the romanticised pen pictures of the drover's life painted by Banjo Paterson and others. Wally Dowling, to whom this version is attributed, was well qualified to assert,

That the drover's life has pleasures That you wouldn't want to know.

Dowling spent much of his life taking cattle down the Canning stock route, linking the south Kimberleys with Wiluna, in Western Australia. It was a difficult route, of 1100 sand hills but only fifty-two wells.

The early overlanders were men seeking adventure and fortune through the taking of stock to new country for speculation or for permanent settlement. After the eventual successful establishment of the frontier stations, an essential element of the pastoral industry was the movement of cattle 'closer in' to market or to better country, where the cattle could be fattened and 'finished'. This was the specified work of the drovers. They were men, and sometimes women, who spent lifetimes on 'the roads', as the stock routes were known. Their nominal homes were the drovers' towns near stock routes — towns like Winton, Camooweal, Boulia, Katherine, Alice Springs, Halls Creek. For the off season, the hotter and wetter months of the year, the drovers would return to their families and let their plant of horses go on the town common for a few months. Then, when the mustering season got under way on the cattle stations, the drovers would be contacted by owners or agents and offered the charge of mobs to be moved.

Most of the drovers were born to this life. Their early experience might be gained on stations, and then the aspiring 'boss drover' would serve his time under a respected and experienced master. Before a man could become a contract drover in his own right, he needed horses and equipment, and then the confidence of an owner who might give him a mob. New drovers would be tried out on small mobs and short trips; if they passed the test, then they would be given the more profitable larger mobs and longer trips, as opportunity arose. It was the ambition of the drover to cement a connection with a large owner who could provide regular work and long trips, or alternatively, several shorter trips in one season.

Droving contracts would provide for payment at the end of the trip at a rate based on numbers in the mob and distance travelled. Theoretically, drovers were quite well paid, but very few were ever able to accumulate any capital.

Once delivery was taken at the beginning of a trip, the boss drover assumed complete responsibility for the cattle until they were counted over to the owner's agent at the trip's end. It was a big responsibility and, because of this, the best drovers were cool-headed men. Worrying types often drove their cattle too hard, transmitted their nervousness to the beasts and were difficult to work with.

Having gained a contract, the drover had to put together men and equipment. After the 'boss', the key man was the horse tailer. Upon him depended the condition of the horses, and making a good start in the mornings. It was the horse tailer's job to have enough horses for the day ready to be caught and saddled before the mob began to stir at first light. During the day, the horse tailer had to find water and grass for the spare horses, and in dry seasons, this often meant detours, or even camping with the horses overnight on a small patch of grass two or three kilometres from the main camp. The horse tailer often did not see a great deal of the other men, but then he asked for, and usually got, more money for his demanding and solitary work. Aborigines often made splendid horse tailers, because of their natural skill in the bush and their ability to recognise the tracks of any horse in the camp.

The Drover's Life

Attributed to Wally Dowling but in fact written by Bruce Forbes Simpson.*

As I write this little ditty
Perhaps I'm feeling blue,
For the swag is wet and sodden
And the fly has blown in too.
The rain is pouring heavy,
The wind is bloody chill,
And I rather feel like howling
With the dingo on the hill.
No doubt this life is thrilling,
Beneath the desert sun and stars,
When your fitting sole companions
Are a mob of mad galahs.
Then the old joke comes to memory,
It was written long ago,
That the drover's life has pleasures
That the townsfolk never know.

When you're sitting on a rooter
With a greenhide monkey halt,
A quiet horse they tell you,
But perhaps he'll buck and bolt,
So you hit him in the shoulders
With a pair of three inch spurs,
Next thing you know you're sitting
In a patch of bloody burrs.
And when you're riding round the greenhides
On a dark and stormy night,
You see the white horns glisten
In the lightning's ghostly light,
And you shiver as you wonder
If they jump which way they'll go.
Yes, the drover's life has pleasures
That the townsfolk never know.

When you're coming down the Canning
Where the lonely stages are,
And the owner comes to meet you
In his brand new motor car,
And the dust he raises mingles
With that churned up by the feet
Of the hides that you are droving
Some of which perhaps he'll eat,
And when you're whipping water
Till your bellows nearly burst

And your water camel joeys
And your bullocks cry from thirst,
When you're tangling with the cleanskins
In the dust and in the heat,
And a big mick with a grievance
Makes a beeline for your seat,
You try to make the fence
But the mick's got too much toe,
Ah, yes, the drover's life has pleasures
That the townsfolk never know.

Where the feed is mostly scanty
And the waterholes are dry,
The squatter's sitting on your back,
It's enough to make you cry.
You battle down a dusty stage
To a well that's broken down,
Or a tank shot full of bullets
By yokels from the town,
And they wonder why you hit the grog
And curse their lousy stations,
Why many a man has cut his throat
In sheer desperation.
So you reckon that you'll chuck it in,
Give something else a go.
Yes the drover's life has pleasures
That the townsfolk never know.

Now the tucker's pretty tasty
On the Canning track you know.
When the flies have had a gutful
The meat ants have a go.
And when you cut the babbler's brownie
It's best to shut your eyes,
For it's hard to tell the difference
Between the currants and the flies.
So let this be a warning
To you fellows from the town,
Who want to go a droving
Where the bullocks all come down.
For if you go a droving
You very soon will know,
That the drover's life has pleasures
That you wouldn't want to know.

Cooks were frequently older men, no longer able to undertake stock work. Often though, they were specialised craftsmen who had done nothing else. They had to understand how a camp worked and when to have food ready at the right times. Food was limited, at least before the advent of motor vehicles and tinned stuffs, to fresh and salt meat and damper, with occasional fresh vegetables. The cook had to be prepared to help the boss kill and cut up a beast. After the kill, the choicest cuts would be reserved for cooking and eating fresh, or part-cooked to preserve them. In cooler weather, meat could be kept fresh for as long as a week, provided it was wrapped in bags during the day and exposed to the cooler air at night. The meat which was not selected to be used while fresh would be rubbed with coarse salt and then carried in bags. Meals were therefore limited to grilled, stewed, boiled or curried meat, hot or cold, and served with generous helpings of tea and damper. Good cooks would create many variations on the basic theme, particularly if they could procure additional ingredients and condiments, such as rice, sago, pickles, sauces, jam and golden syrup, flavouring essences, currants, custard powder and dried fruits.

The stockmen employed by the boss drover could be young men from cattle stations looking for experience or adventure, men from bush towns simply seeking a job, or Aborigines from a mission or government settlement. Some of these men gave droving away after one or two trips, while others stuck at it all their lives.

The number of men required varied with the size of the mob — a big mob might require ten men, while four men would be the bare minimum for even a very small mob.

The basic equipment for a droving plant was simple and limited. Normally the bosses provided saddles and bridles. Food, cooking gear, water and sundry equipment had to be carried. Small wagons (wagonettes) or buggies were favoured, as they made life much easier for the cook and the camp generally. In more recent years, four-wheel drive motor vehicles and trucks came into use and certainly they enabled more material to be carried and did not require good grass. However, they did require fuel. The other alternative was pack horses — essential in heavy, sandy or channel country or in thick scrub. With the pack horse plant, at least five pack animals would be needed, each to carry two packs of between twenty-five and thirty-five kilograms weight. Two packs might contain fresh foodstuffs and cooking gear; three others would contain spare rations, including flour, sugar, salt, jam and sauce; one would contain meat; two would contain such items as horse shoes, hobble chains, nails, shoeing tools and tools for repairing saddlery, while one horse would carry two water canteens, each of about twenty litres. Packs had to be carefully balanced — laying out and loading the packs was a time consuming job for cook and horse tailer. Swags were carried on the top of the packs.

Cooking gear was simple — say two camp ovens, two large billies and a meat bucket. Tin pannikins were usually provided but most men had their own quart pots. A few tin or enamel plates were provided but these were seldom used, as most men would cut a slice of damper and a slice of meat, then use the damper slice as a plate.

Each man had to supply his own swag, which comprised a waterproof canvas tarpaulin as

---

*This poem *The Drover's Life* was found in the possessions of drover Wally Dowling after his death, and it was assumed that he had written the poem. It has since been established that the poem was written by Bruce Forbes Simpson, another drover. Dowling had had some of his own poetry published under the pen-name 'Desert Rat', so it was reasonable for his family to think that he had also written *The Drover's Life*, for the words certainly fitted his rough, tough style. As is common among bushmen, though, he had simply learned Simpson's poem, and substituted references to the Canning Stock Route, where he was a legendary figure. Bruce Simpson's pen-name is 'Lancewood' and most of his droving was done across the Barkly Tableland in the Northern Territory. Simpson's poetry ranges right across the board in terms of mood, and his succinct appreciation of the outback is probably only matched by Ogilvie. Bruce Simpson has twice won The Bronze Swagman Award for Bush Verse sponsored by the Winton Tourist Promotion Association. That Association has published Simpson's poems, along with those of many other fine outback poets.

a swag cover and groundsheet, two double blankets and a spare clothes bag. Drovers slept on the ground with a windbreak of bushes on the windward side of the fire in cold weather. In wet weather, the swag covers were used as a tent, or all hands might shelter under the wagonette or large tarpaulin.

The drovers' day usually started about two hours before daylight, when the man on watch came into the camp and roused the horse tailer and the cook. All three would get a pannikin of tea out of the billy on the fire. Then the horse tailer would pick up a bridle and whip and disappear into the darkness to bring in the horses, so that those to be used that day were ready for the stockmen at first light. The cook would liven up the fire, put the billies and quart pots on to boil and, if he had fresh meat, cook up some steaks. They would be grilled on the coals, or fried in a camp oven. If there was no fresh meat, the previous night's stew or curry might be warmed up.

By this time, it would be getting light and the Morning Star would be fading. A whisper would run through the mob. Most of the cattle would be standing up by now and gradually they would move off to feed. The man on watch would let them feed away, keeping them headed in the right direction. If conditions were right, the mob might feed along for half the morning without having to be driven at all.

Back at the camp, the horse tailer would have brought in the horses. The men would have caught their mounts and ridden out to take over from the watchman. The last watch was often the privilege of the boss, who could get an unbroken night's sleep. However, it could be a long watch if the horse tailer was late in with the horses. When relieved, the last watchman would ride back to the camp for a drink of tea and then breakfast. In the bitter cold of a winter sunrise on the inland plains, he would have to thaw his hands over the fire before he could cut his meat and damper.

The cattle would feed along in the early part of the morning and later, they would move more quickly and string out. By eleven o'clock, the cattle should have reached the spot previously described by the boss to the cook and horse tailer, as the place for the dinner camp. All going well, the cook and horse tailer should have arrived at the dinner camp in time to have the billies boiling when the cattle arrived. But perhaps there were rogue horses in the plant. These would cause the cook and horse tailer long delays, particularly if the plant were using pack horses.

Once at the dinner camp site, the cattle would be steadied and settled down. The men with the cattle would ride into the camp for dinner (drovers never speak of lunch). One man would be left on watch with the cattle. Dinner would comprise damper and cold meat cut by each man from supplies put out by the cook at breakfast time. This cut dinner could be carried in each man's saddlebag.

When all the men had had dinner and a good drink of tea, the cook and horse tailer would pack up and leave for the night's camp site. The night camp would ideally be on a good, open flat with little scrub and a stout tree to tie up the night horses.

The cattle would be moved off the dinner camp at about two o'clock. If there was water, they would drink before leaving the dinner camp. Then they would be allowed to feed along, straight to the night camp. If the dinner camp was dry, the cattle would be walked along until they could be put on to water in the late afternoon. After drinking, they would feed along to the night camp, preferably arriving before dusk.

Meanwhile, the horse tailer would have hobbled his spare horses out on the best feed available. He would bring in wood for the cook, or help him gather dry manure in places where there was no firewood. Then, the horse tailer was 'off duty' until it was time for him to catch and tie up the night horses. By tradition, the horse tailer would then take the first watch, as he had to be first up in the morning. This first watch would start about eight o'clock.

Watching was always the most unpopular task in droving, but all hands except the cook had to do their share. When watching, the man had to know and listen for the language of the mob. Sighs and friendly moans meant no trouble, while a few bellows around the other side of the mob might signify cattle walking away from the main mob. They would have to be turned back into the mob. Constant bellowing usually indicated thirsty, unsettled cattle, needing special vigilance.

It was the usual thing to sing or chant when moving around the cattle on watch. This alerted the cattle to the approach of horse and rider and was said to prevent the cattle from taking sudden fright. But the main advantage was with the boss — if he awoke during the night and heard singing, he would know that the watchman was not asleep.

The length of watches depended on the number of men in the camp and the number of hours of darkness. Usually, the watch was three hours, or a shade less, but on a wet or stormy night, watches might have to be doubled, and each man would be twice as long away from his swag.

Cattle on the roads would frequently be restless between about one and three o'clock in the morning, but would then lie down and sleep until daylight. This was the dangerous time — the worst 'rushes' always started when cattle were lying down. A rush was an uncontrolled, panic stricken flight of cattle off the camp. The Americans would call it a stampede, but no self-respecting Australian would ever use such language.

A rush was something feared by all drovers, as it could be very dangerous to both men and cattle. Often, the cause of a rush was obvious — dingoes, kangaroos, rats or rabbits getting into a mob, or a night horse shaking itself so that the saddle flaps rattled. On other occasions, cattle would 'jump' for no apparent reason. Some drovers speak of cattle sensing trouble in other mobs which might be a day's stage or even further away. Others speak of 'drummy ground' in lime-stone country, where subterranean caverns cause echoes and vibrations on the surface. Some mobs might rush on the first or second night and might continue rushing until delivery. Such cattle would certainly lose a good deal of condition, and many could be lost or killed. Some breeds were said to rush more than others, while cattle from some stations were known to be particularly prone to rushing.

The best ally the drover had during a rush, or at any other time, was a good night horse. These animals were specialists, getting to know their work as well, or better, than those who rode them. Good night horses would amble around the cattle at a slow walk, but they were always alert and would prick their ears at the first sign of anything out of order. Frequently, the night horse would spot a beast moving away from the mob and move after it without any direction from the rider. If the cattle 'jumped' and a rush started, the night horse would be transformed into a cup winner. Sure-footed and keen sighted, they would race to the lead to turn the rushing cattle. Wise riders let a good horse have its head, especially in scrub. Invariably, they found that the night horse would take them through without a scratch.

So the drover's life went on, day after day, in all weathers, with quiet and wild cattle. Every mob had its characters, individual cattle that would be recognised and acquire names after a day or two. As the destination was approaching, the drovers felt that they were owed a good night's sleep. At the end of the trip, delivery was given with a sigh of relief, but with some sadness at parting with old friends in the mob.

The Drover's Boy

The overlanding of cattle to establish the stations of the north, the day to day operation of these stations, the droving trips with the annual turn off from the stations — none of this would have been possible without the use of Aboriginal labour. Disastrous though the invasion of cattle into the Aboriginal domain undoubtedly was, it could be argued that the beef industry afforded the Aboriginal the best compromise between the pre-contact tribal situation and extermination, or complete absorption into the white man's world.

The early years on the pastoral frontier were everywhere years of violent conflict, as Aborigines were inexorably forced to yield their country to cattle. In the more closely settled districts, this meant that Aborigines 'died out', but in the north, black people could at least physically survive the less intense pressure of stocking the poorer country which would only support much lower stocking densities. The Aborigines who survived usually came into the homesteads for food which they had previously been able to get by hunting. In exchange for this food, minimal shelter, and the trinkets of the white man, they provided the greater part of the labour needed to operate the stations. This arrangement enabled them to remain near their own country, 'go walkabout', maintain their ceremonies during the off season months in the beef industry, and to work with dignity at a craft in which they excelled and took great pride. White pastoralists, for their part, recognised that their stations would not be viable without this low cost labour force and so a relationship of mutual dependence grew.

The contribution of Aboriginal men to all of this has been well recorded in prose and verse, but *The Drover's Boy* is a sensitive tribute to the almost forgotten and wilfully obscured contribution of the black women of the outback. The song was inspired by circumstances observed as early as 1882 by W.J. Sowden, who recorded on a trip through the Northern Territory: 'At the Port Darwin Camp there was brought under notice a custom which is too much in vogue amongst those people who drive cattle over from Queensland. We met one of them who had a little black, dressed in boy's clothing, travelling with him as a servant. It transpired that this little fellow was really a girl, and what her life must be I know nothing of. In the particular case I refer to I suppose it must be comfortable enough, for I believe the master is a good-hearted man, but in most cases these feminine boys are the victims of their master's debasing passions. That is the fact, and I do not see why the matter should be minced. There has been too much mincing of it already. Some of these thoughtless bushmen have, in the stealing of their black servants, had "brushes" with the male relatives of the latter and shot them down. The natives make reprisals, and sometimes kill guilty and at other times innocent men. The white residents in the district then have a "revenge" party, and shoot down a score of blacks or so, and call it English justice.'

These relationships between white men and their 'boys' were disguised against social criticism and the law by dressing the 'boy' in men's clothing. But no one was deceived, as long standing Territorian Alfred Searcy noted in 1907: 'Nearly all the drovers, cattlemen, and stationhands had their "black boys" (gins). No objection was raised by the black men to interference with their women so long as they were not abducted. It is the taking away of the women that has been the cause of so many white men having been rubbed out by the niggers. These women are invaluable to the white cattleman, for, besides the companionship, they become splendid horsewomen, and good with cattle. They are useful to find water, settle the camp, boil the billy, and track and bring in the horses in the morning. In fact, it is impossible to enumerate the advantages of having a good gin "outback". The black women are, as a rule, well treated by those who take them.'

The Drover's Boy by Yvonne Dorward

As the harshness of the frontier's early years mellowed, so some of these relationships evolved into something more than enforced liaisons arising out of necessity and violence. But by then, official moves were under way to outlaw cohabitation between whites and blacks, in the Northern Territory at least. Laws attaching harsh penalties to the practice, and requiring separate upbringing of 'mixed blood' children, were based on a special report by pioneer anthropologist, Professor W. Baldwin Spencer for the Commonwealth Government: 'The practice that obtains only too often of a white man, such as a drover or teamster, travelling over the country with an aboriginal woman whom he has, perhaps, taken out of a camp, or who may have come of her own free will . . . must be stopped.'

But in a land where white women were rare, the new laws were more honoured in the breach than in the observance.

Matt Savage was one of many white men who lived with an Aboriginal woman — but Matt's relationship with his Mudbura wife was distinguished by lawful marriage. Matt Savage knew that 'The aborigines certainly did have their good points — and particularly the women. It is no good saying one thing and meaning another; the outback would still have been in its wild state if it had not been for the lubras.'

Dr P. Bell

'None of us would have come up here and lived like a hermit. Even the married blokes like a bit of variety in their lives. So you might say the lubras were the real pioneers because without them there would have been no settlement — or at least it would have come much more slowly.'

The pioneering era is over and we can now look with maturity and compassion at the women who were the drovers' boys. As we take stock of the realities of our history, we all have an obligation to see that they are not forgotten.

'Some of the women were the survivors of conflicts . . .'

The Drover's Boy

Words & Music: Ted Egan

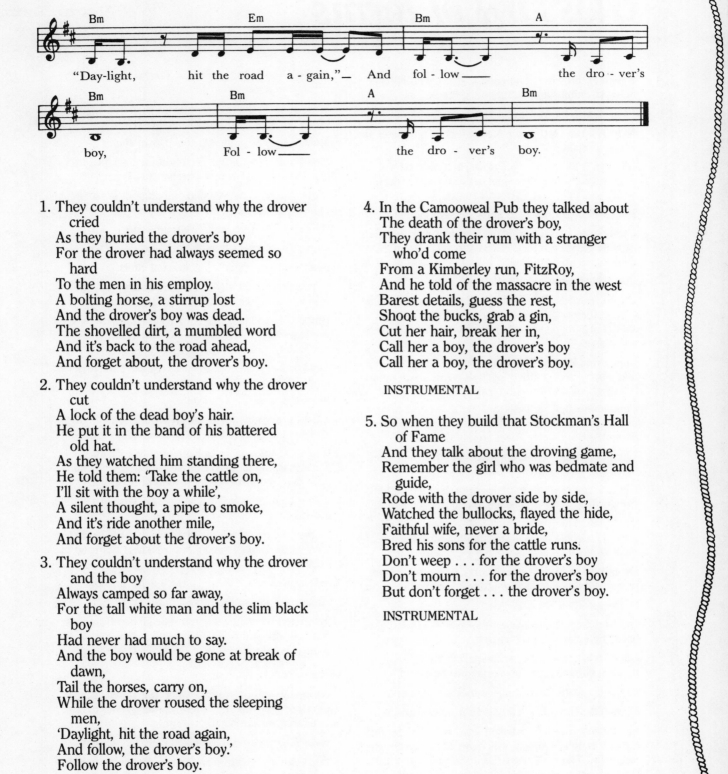

"Day-light, hit the road a-gain,"— And fol-low ___ the dro-ver's boy, Fol-low ___ the dro-ver's boy.

1. They couldn't understand why the drover
   cried
   As they buried the drover's boy
   For the drover had always seemed so
   hard
   To the men in his employ.
   A bolting horse, a stirrup lost
   And the drover's boy was dead.
   The shovelled dirt, a mumbled word
   And it's back to the road ahead,
   And forget about, the drover's boy.

2. They couldn't understand why the drover
   cut
   A lock of the dead boy's hair.
   He put it in the band of his battered
   old hat.
   As they watched him standing there,
   He told them: 'Take the cattle on,
   I'll sit with the boy a while',
   A silent thought, a pipe to smoke,
   And it's ride another mile,
   And forget about the drover's boy.

3. They couldn't understand why the drover
   and the boy
   Always camped so far away,
   For the tall white man and the slim black
   boy
   Had never had much to say.
   And the boy would be gone at break of
   dawn,
   Tail the horses, carry on,
   While the drover roused the sleeping
   men,
   'Daylight, hit the road again,
   And follow, the drover's boy.'
   Follow the drover's boy.

   INSTRUMENTAL

4. In the Camooweal Pub they talked about
   The death of the drover's boy,
   They drank their rum with a stranger
   who'd come
   From a Kimberley run, FitzRoy,
   And he told of the massacre in the west
   Barest details, guess the rest,
   Shoot the bucks, grab a gin,
   Cut her hair, break her in,
   Call her a boy, the drover's boy
   Call her a boy, the drover's boy.

   INSTRUMENTAL

5. So when they build that Stockman's Hall
   of Fame
   And they talk about the droving game,
   Remember the girl who was bedmate and
   guide,
   Rode with the drover side by side,
   Watched the bullocks, flayed the hide,
   Faithful wife, never a bride,
   Bred his sons for the cattle runs.
   Don't weep . . . for the drover's boy
   Don't mourn . . . for the drover's boy
   But don't forget . . . the drover's boy.

   INSTRUMENTAL

Glossary of terms

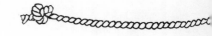

Babbler's brownie. The cook's fruit cake, 'babbler' being rhyming slang for 'babbling brook'.

Blow (take a blow). Have a rest.

Billy. A tin can with a wire handle used to boil water in which to make tea.

Blucher. A name commonly given to blue heeler cattle dogs. As pups they often slept in their owner's Blucher boots.

Buck. A derogatory word applied to Aboriginal men.

Camp oven. A cast iron oven with a wire handle, capable of being buried in coals to effect 'oven' type cooking on an open fire.

Cleanskins. Unbranded cattle.

Cigarette swags. Thin bedrolls. Early drovers used to ensure the swags of their men passed through the spokes of a wagon wheel to minimise the load for their packhorses.

Concertina leggins (leggings). Short, expandable (up and down) soft leather leggings worn over riding boots, especially in rough country.

Condamine Bell. A large bell hung around horse's necks to locate them in heavy scrub when grazing. From the Condamine River area of Queensland.

Damper. A huge scone, cooked either in a camp oven or on the coals of a camp fire.

Dip (the mob). Putting cattle through a 'dip'; a long trough filled with disinfected water designed to kill ticks.

Drovers. People engaged in the long distance movement of stock.

Droughted in. Where stock cannot be moved forward or backward due to lack of water and/or feed.

Duffing (cattle). Stealing.

Drafting. Separating stock for specific purposes, like branding, weaning, selecting a mob for a droving trip.

Galah. A gregarious Australian parrot, but also a nickname applied to a person deemed to be stupid.

Gin. A derogatory word applied to Aboriginal women.

Greenhide. Untanned leather cut from cattle hide.

LC (brand). The LC 5 brand was that used by the Landsborough Company, which owned Bowen Downs originally. The 'five' were Landsborough, Cornish, Buchanan (first manager), Morehead and Young.

MTD (brand). The registered brand of Mt Doreen cattle station, Central Australia.

Monkey holt (hold), **greenhide.** The handgrip near the pommel of a saddle.

Mob. A word used to describe a large, undomesticated group of cattle, as distinct from 'herd'.

Mustering. The gathering together of stock.

Moleskins. The durable, tight-fitting cotton trousers (usually white) worn by Australian stockmen.

Night horse. The reliable, intelligent horse kept tethered at night in case of emergency.

OT Line. The Overland Telegraph Line.

Plant. The drover's horses, pack and riding.

Push. See also 'stage'. A concerted effort.

Paraway (Far Away). The nickname given by Aboriginals to the legendary Nat Buchanan.

Ringers. Stockmen. The Australian equivalent of the word 'cowboy' but Australian stockmen are never called 'cowboys'.

Road trains. Huge motor trucks used to cart stock by road.

Rooter. A horse that bucks.

Riders (on gates) (as in 'Andy's Gone with Cattle'). Timber slats used to lock two wooden gates together.

Rush. The wild, uncontrollable running of cattle, particularly at night. The equivalent of the word 'stampede' but 'stampede' is never used in Australia.

Stages. (e.g. dry stages). The various parts of a cattle droving trip.

Station. A large area of land on which cattle or sheep are grazed. Equals 'ranch' but 'ranch' is not used in Australian parlance.

Selection. A block of land 'selected' for grazing.

Squatter. A large land holder.

Swag. Bedroll and belongings rolled in a canvas sheet and tied with straps.

Tucker. Food.

The 'wet'. The rainy season.

Whipping (water). Drawing water from a well using an animal to 'whip up' the water by pulling ropes to raise and lower buckets simultaneously.

Yeller feller. A person of mixed race.

Yards. Stoutly built post and rail holding areas, used to hold and/or draft cattle and sheep. Equals 'corral' but 'corral' is not used in Australian parlance.

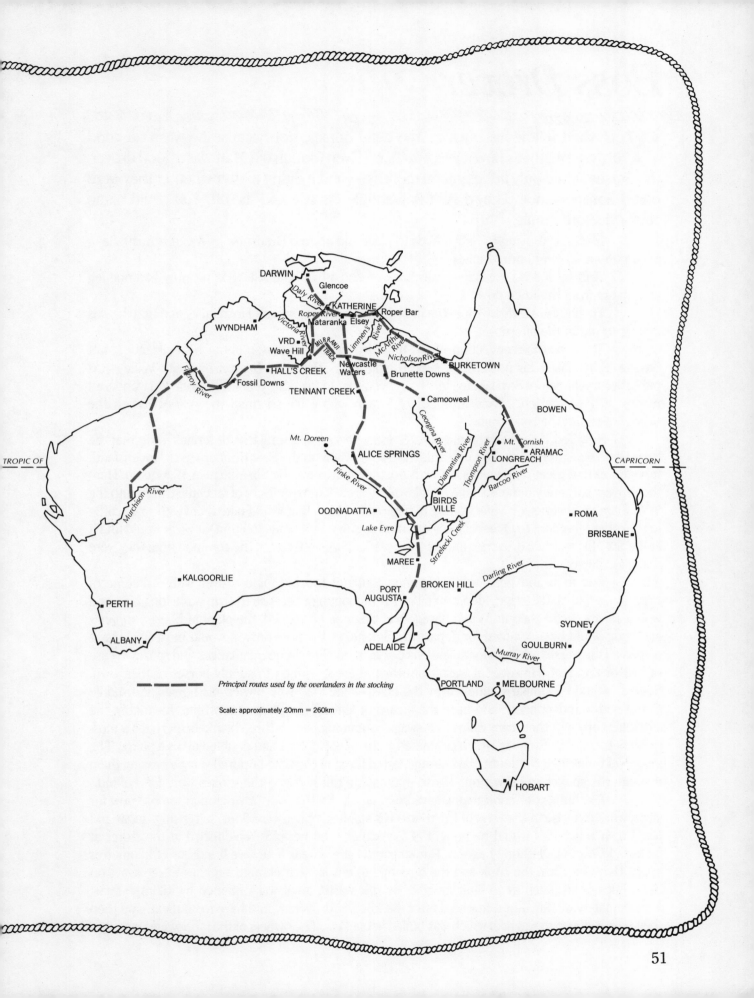

DARWIN
Glencoe
Daly River
KATHERINE
Roper River   Roper Bar
Mataranka Elsey
WYNDHAM
Victoria River
VRD   MURRANJI   *Limmen's River*
Wave Hill   TRACK
McArthur River
Newcastle   *Nicholson River*   BURKETOWN
Waters
HALL'S CREEK   Brunette Downs
Fitzroy River   Fossil Downs   BOWEN
TENNANT CREEK   Camooweal
Georgina River

Mt. Doreen
Diamantina River   Mt. Cornish
ALICE SPRINGS   *Thompson River*   ARAMAC
LONGREACH
TROPIC OF   *Finke River*   *Barcoo River*   CAPRICORN
Murchison River
OODNADATTA   BIRDS   ROMA
VILLE   BRISBANE
Lake Eyre   *Strzelecki Creek*
MAREE
Darling River
KALGOORLIE   PORT   BROKEN HILL
AUGUSTA   SYDNEY
PERTH   GOULBURN
Murray River
ALBANY   ADELAIDE
PORTLAND   MELBOURNE

Principal routes used by the overlanders in the stocking

Scale: approximately 20mm = 260km

HOBART

Boss Drover

'**Y**ou could follow his track by the dead horses, not because he wasn't a good drover, but that's how it was out there. Even though old Matt was a good drover, the horses would only last eighteen months — and it didn't matter whether they were blood horses or not. They'd get "walkabout" disease and die off. You could name your price on a mule.

'Matt was droving from the Alice to places up around Bradshaw in Western Australia, a trip of about fifteen hundred miles.

'And he still rides today — with his one-and-a-half hind legs. (He recently had one leg amputated from the knee down.)

'He had his leg taken off in the morning at the Alice Springs Hospital — and here he was talking to me in the afternoon.'

That was the recollection of old time drover Jack Swanson about his colleague, Matt Savage. Fortunately for posterity, a superb biography, *The Boss Drover*, by Keith Willey, was published a year before Savage died in 1972, aged more than eighty years. The book is a wonderful record of the experiences and attitudes of a man whose life spanned the years between the overlanders and the road trains.

Now Ted Egan has commemorated Matt Savage in a song that describes a trip that the Boss Drover might have made with cattle from somewhere in the East Kimberleys to Queensland. It begins at that great rendezvous of north Australian drovers, the Six Mile near Wyndham. Here the drovers gathered in the Six Mile Hotel while waiting to give delivery of fat cattle driven into the Wyndham meatworks, or while waiting to begin other trips that would take them with store cattle in the other direction, to Queensland's fattening country. Stockmen looking for work would find it at the Six Mile — while drovers could let their plant of horses feed out the common until they were ready for departure.

Two thousand head was a big mob, but not too big for a drover with a lifetime of experience like Matt Savage. Men would be eager to join him because the trip was a long one, and would earn a useful cheque. When Savage had the men he wanted, the plant of horses, supplies and gear would be assembled for departure. Savage, as the boss drover, would most likely have owned all the horses, enough for at least six per man, to allow frequent changes and spares in case of loss or accident. However, it wasn't unheard of for stockmen to supply horses of their own. Saddles would be similarly supplied by the boss — the man who owned his horses and saddle would be too independent and have the means of leaving the plant at any time. Invariably, the stockmen brought their own whips and swags containing two or three blankets, perhaps a mosquito net, and a clothes bag which contained a change of clothes and doubled up as a pillow. The swag had to be thin. No doubt Matt Savage tested them in the time honored way by passing them through the spokes of his wagon. Those that couldn't fit between the spokes were left behind.

The hung-over cook might have been an old time drover or stockman too old now for stock work but wise in the ways of the roads. His staple supplies were flour, salt, rising, sugar and tea. Fresh vegetables would be bought at Wyndham, and perhaps replenished at the stores at Newcastle Waters, Anthony Lagoon, Rankine and Camooweal. They are hundreds of kilometres apart. Between them the cook and the boss had to ensure that enough supplies were always on hand but not so much as to limit mobility or risk waste. Meat was obtained by killing a beast approximately weekly. For a few days after the kill, the drovers would have fresh meat, and then they were reduced to salt beef which was boiled in buckets. The owners of the mob would include a

Matt Savage: Boss Drover. By Mark Egan

number of 'killers' over and above the strict number to be delivered. However, it was a point of honour with Matt Savage (and many others) never to kill a beast from his own mob, but rather to kill a beast which had been dropped from another mob, or one belonging to the station he was passing through. If the beast belonged to the giant English meat company, Vesteys, so much the better.

After leaving Wyndham, Savage would travel with his men and plant to the station from which the cattle were to be taken. There, if all was according to plan, the station stockmen would have the cattle in a mob and ready for counting by Savage and the station manager, as a preliminary to formal delivery to the drover. Again ideally, the station would send its men with the mob for the first one or two days, to help the drovers at a time when the cattle were likely to be touchy and inclined to rush at night.

Then the routine of the trip would begin. Sixteen to twenty kilometres per day along a 2000 kilometre route to the railhead at Dajarra in Queensland; across the Murranji Track, pioneered by Nat Buchanan in 1886, notorious for its dry stages, lancewood and bullwaddy scrub, and for the graves of drovers stricken by malaria in the years before the Flying Doctor; to Newcastle Waters, across the Tablelands route to Anthony Lagoon, and then over the treeless plains bordering Queensland.

Delivery would be given to the owner or his agent when the mob was counted into the railway trucking yards at Dajarra. Matt Savage and his men would be into the bar for a blowout. Already, Matt would be thinking of taking his plant back to the Top End for another mob before the wet season, or perhaps of a trip with horses from the Centre up the Tanami Track to the Kimberleys. That done, he could join his wife and three daughters at his camp in the hills just north of Alice Springs.

The trucking yard at Dajarra. From here the cattle would be railed to coastal meatworks, or to 'inside country' where they would be fattened

Bore on the Murranji Stock Route, was one of a number put down by the Commonwealth Government to eliminate the notorious dry stages with which early overlanders and drovers had to contend

For Matt Savage and many others, the Dajarra Hotel was the oasis at the end of droving trips which may have begun 2000 kilometres away

Matt Savage: Boss Drover

Words & Music: Ted Egan

1. At the Six Mile in Wyndham the word passed a-round,— Matt Savage, the boss dro-ver, has just come to town,— His plant's on the com-mon, he's look-ing for men,— 'Cause he's tak-ing a mob in-to Queens-land.— He's a leg-end in the out-back, he's a man a-mong men, Matt Sav-age, the boss dro-ver, and he's rid-ing a-gain;— Two-thou-sand store bul-locks, wild ones at that, That's the mob that he's tak-ing in-to Queens-land.—

Chorus

Matt Sav-age, the boss dro-ver, he'll take a mob— o-ver, Tak-in' the bul-locks to Queens-land, ah ha! Matt Sav-age, the boss dro-ver, he'll take a mob— o-ver, Tak-ing the bul-locks to Queens-land.—

1. At the Six Mile in Wyndham the word
      passed around
   Matt Savage the Boss Drover has just
      come to town.
   His plant's on the Common, he's looking
      for men
   'Cos he's taking a mob into Queensland.

   He's a legend in the outback, he's a man
      among men,
   Matt Savage the Boss Drover, and he's
      riding again.
   Two thousand store bullocks, wild ones
      at that,
   That's the mob that he's taking into
      Queensland.

   CHORUS
   Matt Savage, the Boss Drover, he'll take
      a mob over
   Taking the bullocks to Queensland ah ha!
   Matt Savage, the Boss Drover, he'll take a
      mob over
   Taking the bullocks to Queensland.

2. Six of us ringers, with cigarette swags
   Signed up by Matt Savage, and we've
      each got six nags,
   The cook's all hung over, but the Boss
      Drover knows
   That he'll travel O.K. into Queensland.

   First night, stars bright, cattle travelling
      well,
   Hear the jingle of the hobbles, hear the
      Condamine Bell,
   Sing a song as we watch them, make the
      buggers lie down
   Or they'll rush all the way into
      Queensland.

   CHORUS
   Matt Savage, the Boss Drover etc.

3. Meat for the packbags as we pass through
      Wave Hill,
   There's a big Vestey's bullock, so we're
      in for the kill,
   Grilled rib-bones tonight by the camp
      fire's light,
   We'll be fit when we finally hit
      Queensland.

   But we're haunted by ghosts on the
      Murranji Track,
   Dead men, dead bullocks, cursed
      outback,

Cattle dry-staging, and the Boss Drover's
   raging,
Hard times on the way into Queensland.

CHORUS
Matt Savage, the Boss Drover, etc.

4. The Murranji's dry, but at Newcastle
      Waters,
   We'll be dancing in the bar with old
      Bullwaddy's daughters,*
   Then it's back in the saddle, keep
      pushing them cattle,
   Gotta take 'em along into Queensland.

   And when the bullocks all rushed, led by
      the big roan,
   Matt Savage on the night-horse, he
      turned them alone,
   He's been on the road now for around
      forty years,
   Boss Drover on the stock routes into
      Queensland.

   CHORUS
   Matt Savage, the Boss Drover etc.

5. Four months on the road, and the
      Tableland's bare,
   It's heat and it's dust and there's flies
      everywhere,
   But when we get to Camooweal we won't
      give a damn and we'll
   Go riding along into Queensland.

   And there's the railway, there's the
      siding, delivery Dajarra,
   Then as quick as a flash we'll be into the
      bar
   Of the pub for a blowout, and a gutful
      of rum,
   'Cos we just brought a mob into
      Queensland.

   CHORUS (twice)
   Matt Savage, the Boss Drover, etc.

* Bullwaddy Bates was a legendary figure who came
onto the Barkly Tableland, acquired several Jingili
women as concubines and set up Beetaloo and OT
Stations. Unlike many of his contemporaries, Bates
(or Bathern, which was his correct name) recognised
his mixed-race children, and bequeathed the
properties to them when he died.

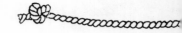

The Goanna Drover

Words & Music: Ted Egan

1. I was drink-in' in the bar of the Birds-ville pub_ when this long skin-ny fel-ler comes in,

Greas-y old mole-skins, con-cer-ti-na leg-gins, On his face was a dev-i-lish grin, Well he

breasts the bar,_ gives a lit-tle "yee-hah," says: "I'm sor-ry that I got no dough, But I'll

spin you a yarn if you buy me a drink, It's a sto-ry that you all should know."

Yes he said he was a dro-ver,_ the fin-est in the land,_ He was

trav-el-ling a-round Aus-tra-li-a, Ten-thou-sand go-an-nas in hand

1. I was drinkin' in the bar of the Birdsville Pub
   When this long skinny feller comes in,
   Greasy old moleskins, concertina leggins
   On his face was a devilish grin.
   Well he breasted the bar, gives a little 'Yee-Har',
   Says: 'I'm sorry that I've got no dough.
   But I'll spin you a yarn if you buy me a beer,
   It's a story that you all should know.'

   CHORUS
   Yes, he said he was a drover, finest in the land,
   He was travelling around Australia, ten thousand goannas in hand.

2. He said: 'I'm drovin' ten thousand goannas,
   Been five years on the track,
   Started up at Cairns where we dipped the mob
   Then we headed for the great outback.
   Went due west to the 'Curry, across them black soil plains
   But we got bogged down at the Isa, and had to fit the goannas with chains.'

   CHORUS
   Yes, he said he was a drover etc.

3. 'Walkin' 'em down the Murranji Track
   The goannas started climbing trees,
   But a drover's got to improvise
   And I solved the problem with ease.
   You see the monsoon rains was due to start, we had no time to lose,
   So I got forty thousand sardine tins and fitted the goannas with shoes.'

CHORUS
Yes, he said he was a drover etc.

4. 'Well we clanked across them gibber plains,
   She's hard on shoes out there,
   But the move paid off in the Channel Country
   'Cos the rivers had filled Lake Eyre.
   So I got an old bull camel, and I showed him who was boss,
   I hit the camel with the old "brick trick" and he waterskied the goannas across.'

CHORUS
Yes, he said he was a drover etc.

5. 'So here I am at the Birdsville Pub
   And if you buy me another drink,
   I'll tell you about me future plans,
   That's fair enough wouldn't you think?'
   He said: 'I'll have a rum this time, a double, 'Good Luck, Yes, Cheers'
   Well I'm off now, mates, 'So Long, Hooroo' I'll be in Hobart within two years.'

6. We called: 'Hang on a minute,
   We can see you're a bit of a "star"
   But drovin' goannas to Tassie, mate,
   That's takin' things a bit too far.
   How would you get them goannas right across Bass Strait?'
   He flashed up all his devilish grin and said:
   'I'm not goin' that way, mate!!!!!'

CHORUS
Yes, he said he was a drover etc.

The Goanna Drover hits Birdsville. By Mark Egan

Ben Hartigan

A poem by Mary Durack

'Well, I'll be pushing along', Ben Hartigan says,
Tightens the girth and pulls himself onto his mule.
'What! Not wait for a beer?'
'No fear!'
Says Hartigan, and looks at the sun.
'Think I come down in the last shower?
'Me plant's been waiting all day
'She'll be dark be about an hour.'
And he pulls down the brim of his hat and rides away.

'What age do you reckon he'd be, old Hartigan?'
'Lord knows. Eighty. Or some say over.'
'He's just about had it, I'd say. Doesn't look so clever.'
'Why don't they pension him off? He's too old for a drover.'
But who are 'they' to pension Ben Hartigan?
Who was never beholden to any of 'them' — not ever?

A parchment over the bones is Hartigan's skin,
His lips tight stretched to a grin
That owes little mirth.
Remember that face,
For he's nearly the last of his race
Ben Hartigan, and his kind was the salt of the earth.

He's touchy about his sight, old Hartigan,
Dark specs fixed on with thread
Cover potch-opal eyes
The rims blood-red
From what he calls 'a touch of sandy blight'
And blames the flies.
'But I'll follow a track like a black,' he says,
In a fair light.

He likes a yarn when the grog's flowing, old Hartigan.
If you get him going
He'll talk about Greenhide Sam
And the yeller feller,
Of Bullocky Kinivan who packed the mail,
And Nat Buchanan with his green umbrella
And old Tom 'Stone the Crows' Cahill.

'Ah,' says Hartigan, 'them was the days.
'Fellers were tough then, and tireless,
'No affectations. You lived or died, see?
'No half-ways. Or complications.
'There wasn't the set-up then for saving lives
'No Flying Doctor or pedal wireless
'Or pesterin' wives.'

'White women,' says Hartigan,
'Amenities and the rest of it,
'They'd drive you crazy.
'I reckon it was us blokes had the best of it,
'Like me with young Daisy.
'Thirty years back she was,
'But I don't forget her.
'Faithful! She'd of been with me yet,
'If only they'd let her.'

'I had a fall once out mustering round Mount Hurst,
'Busted me collar bone and broke a shin,
'After three days what with the flamin' thirst
'The ants attackin' and the crows black round me,
'I just about gives in. I know darn well
'The only hope I got in hell is that young gin.
'She told me after it was the birds brought her,
'But she'd of battled on 'til she died or found me,
'And perished before she'd touch that water.

'But then the law steps in and has to "save" her',
Says Hartigan. 'Though she never gone much on hymns,
'Or the togs they gave her —
'Some white woman's cast-off dress for her dungarees,
'Shut up inside a fence, boiled hash and stew,
'And prayin' on her knees. It never made much sense,
'When all she asked was her man, and a horse, and the life she knew.'

'I told them pretty straight,' says Hartigan,
'Without you let her be, she'll have that kid and die!
'I know her, see? I said.'
'But they got hearts like stone
'I had to get them cattle in alone,
'And when I makes back after, it's too late.
'She's dead.'

'That nice little run I used to count on owning
'Got swallowed up long ago in the next estate.
'It was always a big man's country. No use moaning',
Says Hartigan, 'Against your cut with fate.
'It's something to be still around, a drover,
'These times when speed's the general way of things,
'And trucks and airy-planes is taking over
'And beef on the hoof is beef on wheels or wings.'

'Joy-ridin'! That's all they're fit for, this generation,
'Take young Hartigan now, truckin' cattle Fitzroy into Broome,
'One day against ten in the saddle, or damn near,
'And they give him a fair deal there,
'I wouldn't see his month's cheque inside a year.
'Catch him knuckling down on a station
'When he can set up behind the wheel there,
'Blastin' his old man off the road to make room.'

'But mind you, he's nobody's fool, young Ben there,
Says Hartigan. 'There's no white going to make a butt of him,
'No fear! He got learned in a school,
'Holds his own with the men there.
'You can tell that be the cut of him.'

'Well, I gotta compete with them motors now, and that's that,'
Says Hartigan, and pulls down his hat.
'Can't be hangin' round them bars now,
'With me plant waitin' some place out on the flat.'
He fixes a stirrup and grins as he tightens the girth.
Remember that face — for he's nearly the last of his race,
Ben Hartigan, and his kind was the salt of the earth.

Cattle going in

None was better qualified to write of the changing methods of moving cattle than Doreen Braitling. Born in England in 1906, she came to Alice Springs as a small child with her family, who had been lured to the Centre by their pioneering relative Fred Raggatt. After working on the Overland Telegraph Line, Raggatt ran a store in Alice Springs and struggled to establish Glen Helen station in the western MacDonnell Ranges.

Educated behind the old gaol in Alice Springs after Mrs Ida Standley opened a school there in 1914, Doreen Crook (as she then was) matriculated into the university of hard knocks when her family headed north at the end of World War I. They were making for the wolfram fields at Wauchope, but prices collapsed before the family arrived. During the retreat south along the Telegraph Line the Crooks were 'droughted in' for a time at Wycliffe Well — conditions on the track were so dry that it was unsafe to travel forward or back. Making a virtue out of necessity the Crooks obtained the licence to draw water from the well. This entitled them to charge drovers of travelling stock one penny per head for cattle and threepence per head for horses and camels watered at the well. In return they had to keep the well and its facilities in good repair.

Not long before her death in February 1979 Mrs Braitling spoke of her teenage years at Wycliffe Well. 'My sister Kathleen and I worked the well. There were two sixteen gallon buckets in the well, and they were pulled up and down by the operation of a wire rope passing over head wheels fixed to a head frame built on top of the dump of the well. The rope passed from the head wheels to a whip, and a draught animal was harnessed to the rope between the idler wheel and the bull wheel. The draught animal — it could have been a horse or camel or working bullock — was led forward and back. As it pulled the rope one way, one bucket would be pulled from the bottom of the well toward the top while the other bucket would be lowered.'

Two people were needed to pull the water. One would stand on top of the dump, while the other would lead the draught animal. When the full bucket reached the top, the person on top of the well would signal the other to pause. During this pause the full bucket was steadied and then its contents were tipped into a receiving trough. Meanwhile, the empty bucket was at the bottom of the well. When the bucket hit the water a flap valve in the bottom would open and the bucket would begin to fill. Another signal would be given, and the draught animal would be turned around to walk in the opposite direction.

The distance the animal and its leader had to walk was equal to the depth of the well. Some wells were about twenty metres deep, with good supplies of water, but others were much deeper and only had poor supplies. For example, Deep Well, south of Alice Springs, was seventy metres deep. Pulling water from these very deep wells was a slow process. If a mob of any size had to be watered you might have to start a day or two before to fill the storage tank ahead of the arrival of the mob.

It was because of the limitations of the wells that mobs on the stock routes in the Centre were kept to a maximum of about 300. You just couldn't water a bigger mob than that.

These wells had been constructed either along the Overland Telegraph Line when it was built in 1870-2, or during a South Australian Government improvement programme in the '80s. Thereafter though, there was no development of water facilities until long after the Commonwealth took control of the Northern Territory in 1911. The South Australian authorities preferred to spend their available funds on deep bores along the Birdsville Track to ensure that cattle from Queensland's Channel Country would move south toward the Adelaide market.

Frequently drovers had to leave at the wells weaker animals and calves which could not keep up with the main mob. Doreen and Kathleen Crooks would 'poddy' these animals and gradually they built up a herd of their own around Wycliffe Well. With these the family established Singleton Station.

Doreen Crooks married Top End drover Bill Braitling and for years her matrimonial home was a bough shed at a wolfram mining camp 400 kilometres north west from Alice Springs. Bill Braitling named a nearby mountain after his bride, and 'Mount Doreen' was to be the name of their station as the Braitlings gradually turned away from mining to cattle. Then, as now, Mount Doreen was on the extreme edge of Northern Territory pastoral settlement.

At first Mount Doreen had been too remote to practically run cattle, but in the late 1930s the Northern Territory Administration gradually opened up the 'North West' stock route between the railhead at Alice Springs and Tanami and the Granites. By 1939 cattle could be walked in from Mount Doreen on this route, being watered on the way at government bores so placed that mobs could get a drink every second day.

In her later life Doreen Braitling enjoyed some of the comforts which her long years of battling had earned for her. One of her main interests became the preservation of Australia's pioneering heritage, both through the written record and through physical protection of the buildings and artifacts of earlier days and ways. Her beautiful poem *Cattle Going In* recorded what she saw of the changing ways of droving. These changes were made possible or inevitable by the development of large road trains, the construction of 'beef roads', changing industrial awards concerning the employment of Aboriginal labour by drovers, and by drought.

In 1956-7 the Federal Government commenced a major road construction programme to give improved road access to most of Australia's cattle country. First, formed earth roads were built, then these were sheeted with gravel in difficult sections, and then many roads were sealed.

The results were dramatic. In 1956-7 only 3.3% (4480 cattle) of the Territory's total 'turn-off' was moved by road train. By 1960-1 this had increased to 55% (93 151 cattle). Over the next few years drought in Central Australia closed most stock routes, and the road trains took over completely, and from then on trips for cattle going in to the meatworks or railhead were measured in hours rather than weeks.

Doreen Braitling felt that the vanished band of old time drovers should not be forgotten.

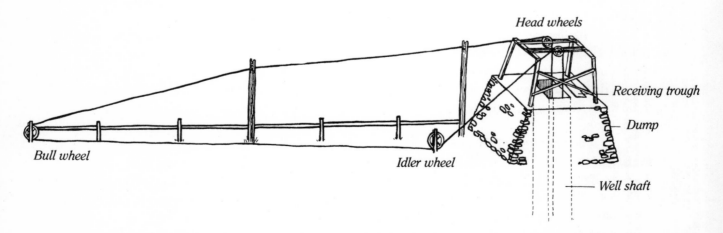

Well and whip as installed along overland telegraph line and other stock routes in Central and South Australia

A camel 'whipping' water from a well, Central Australia

Well headworks, Overland Telegraph Line NT

Wave Hill cattle at Alice Springs NT 1903. Note the predominant white colouring on the cattle in this Shorthorn mob. Cattlemen later bred away from this lighter colouring, believing that it predisposed cattle to skin irritation and disease in hot North Australia

Well bucket of the kind used to pull water on many stock routes until quite recent times

Doreen Braitling by Jeanette Cook

Cattle Going In

Words: Doreen Braitling. **Music:** *Ted Egan*

1. Cattle going in
   From mulga scrub and saltbush plain
   Cattle going in
   We mustered them in dry and rain
   Cattle going in
   We're yarding cattle from the west
   Swing wide the gates and draft the best
   Let down the rails and 'Bush' the rest
   Cattle going in.

2. Cattle going in
   At break of day we loaded up
   Cattle going in
   Now road trains roll, the last is gone
   Cattle going in
   Red clouds rise, they seem to burn
   Behind the big wheels as they churn
   The ancient desert dust astern
   Of cattle going in.

3. Cattle going in
   With MTD on every hide*
   Cattle going in
   There's open country every side
   Of cattle going in
   Two hundred miles or more to go
   Through hills and creeks where gumtrees
     grow
   No time to camp or take a blow
   With cattle going in.

* On Northern Territory cattle stations all registered brands must be of three letters, one of which must be 'T' for 'Territory'. MTD is the registered brand of Mt Doreen Station, 420 kilometres north-west from Alice Springs. Doreen Braitling, who wrote the words of 'Cattle Going In' is the 'Doreen' after whom the station is named.

4. Cattle going in
   The big trucks sway along the tracks
   With cattle going in
   The dust falls thick upon the backs
   Of cattle going in
   Motors turning sweet and right
   Southern Cross clear and bright
   And silent drivers ride the night.
   With cattle going in.

5. Cattle going in
   The shades of old time drovers stare
   At cattle going in
   Their ghostly horses snort and glare
   At cattle going in
   Road trains roaring overland
   Their drivers couldn't understand
   The months it took that vanished band
   With cattle going in.

After a few weeks on the road, most cattle settle down to the daily routine of morning and afternoon travel, punctuated by the dinner camp

Johnny Stewart

Johnny Stewart, Drover

In 1967, a young London born man came to this country, expecting to find the land and people of Australian legend. Chris Buch didn't find the bush until he moved from Queensland's Gold Coast to Mount Isa in 1970. He had been interested in folk music since his arrival in Australia and, in Mount Isa, he discovered the ballads of the outback. He discovered too, that the drovers of song and verse had not all given way to road trains and old age. Several were still walking cattle down the Georgina and Diamantina stock routes, as drovers had done for a century. Chris Buch resolved to collect and preserve the traditions of these drovers and decided to join one of them on a trip.

An experienced station manager friend recommended to Chris, 'Go with Johnny Stewart. He still does things the right way'. Contact was made with Johnny through Rocklands Station, which regularly employed the drover to take cattle down into southwest Queensland to other stations owned by the same company. These movements are part of the time honored practice of taking store cattle from breeding country in the north to softer, sweeter grasslands for fattening. At the same time, the cattle are being moved closer to railheads and eventual markets.

Nowadays, roadtrains move almost all these cattle, but some owners still choose to have them walked to their 'closer in' destination.

These owners may control a chain of stations along the chosen route, and thus the cattle

The dinner camp fire for the drover

can be taken in very easy stages, without regard to the law which requires them to move sixteen kilometres per day. While with the drover, the cattle are being handled and are becoming used to man. After a trip on foot, they settle down immediately they are let go on new country, whereas a trip on a road train does nothing to quieten wild cattle bred in remote areas. In good seasons, cattle with careful drovers should gain, or at least hold condition, while on the road trains they can suffer bruising and death. Geography is important too, as some trips can be shorter over the direct route taken by a drover than by the main roads to which the road trains are confined.

For all of these reasons, it is likely that there will always be enough work for those men who still have the skill to walk the cattle down.

In July 1981, Chris Buch joined Johnny Stewart with a mob of 1500 hundred Rocklands cattle which were to be driven down the Georgina, across the Diamantina and then to Tanbar Station, near Windorah on the Cooper. The whole trip would take thirteen weeks, and Chris was able to spend ten days of that time with the cattle as they passed through the Urandangie district. His beautiful ballad, 'Johnny Stewart, Drover' was the result.

Drovers with Johnny Stewart, on dinner camp

Horses in Johnny Stewart's plant, feeding on dinner camp

Johnny Stewart's mob, Thompson River, below Longreach, Qld

Johnny Stewart: Drover

Words & Music: Chris Buch

1. The mob is dipped,___ the plant has start - ed out,___

Leav - in' Rock - land's dust - y yards___ be - hind them,___ The

whips are crack - ing and the dro - vers shout, And

on the Queens ___ - land stock - routes you will find them.___

Drov - in' ways___ have been like this___ for years,

Mod - ern times___ don't mean these days are o - ver, ___ For

die - sel road - trains can - not know___ the steers, Or

walk 'em down___ like John - ny Stew - art, dro - ver.___

Chorus

On the banks of ___ the Georg - i - na___ down the Dia - man - ti - na,___ To

where the grass___ is green - er, down in New South Wales,___

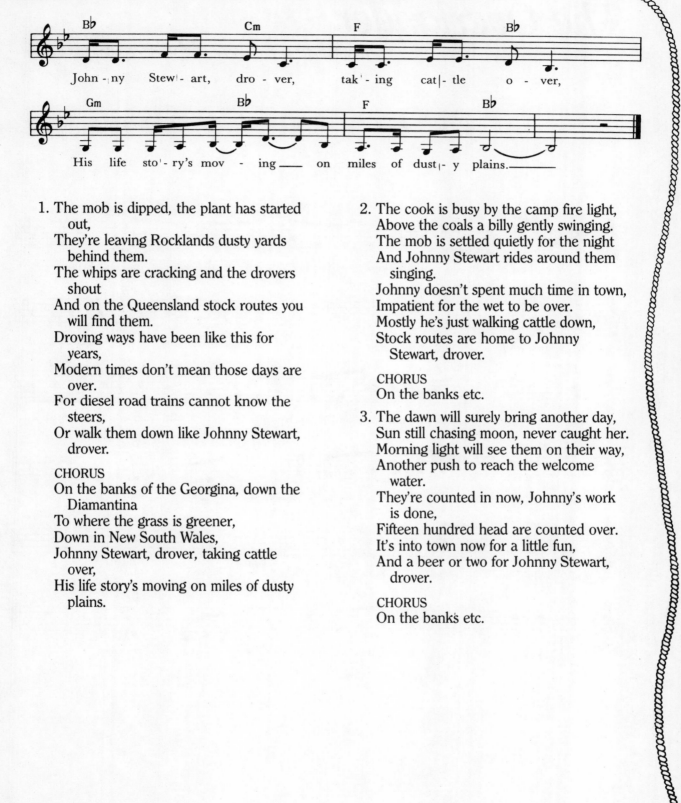

Johnny Stewart, drover, takin' cattle over, His life story's moving on miles of dusty plains.

1. The mob is dipped, the plant has started out,
They're leaving Rocklands dusty yards behind them.
The whips are cracking and the drovers shout
And on the Queensland stock routes you will find them.
Droving ways have been like this for years,
Modern times don't mean those days are over.
For diesel road trains cannot know the steers,
Or walk them down like Johnny Stewart, drover.

CHORUS
On the banks of the Georgina, down the Diamantina
To where the grass is greener,
Down in New South Wales,
Johnny Stewart, drover, taking cattle over,
His life story's moving on miles of dusty plains.

2. The cook is busy by the camp fire light,
Above the coals a billy gently swinging.
The mob is settled quietly for the night
And Johnny Stewart rides around them singing.
Johnny doesn't spent much time in town,
Impatient for the wet to be over.
Mostly he's just walking cattle down,
Stock routes are home to Johnny Stewart, drover.

CHORUS
On the banks etc.

3. The dawn will surely bring another day,
Sun still chasing moon, never caught her.
Morning light will see them on their way,
Another push to reach the welcome water.
They're counted in now, Johnny's work is done,
Fifteen hundred head are counted over.
It's into town now for a little fun,
And a beer or two for Johnny Stewart, drover.

CHORUS
On the banks etc.

The Overlander

Traditional: Arrangement: The Mucky Ducky Bush Band

1. Now there's a trade you all know well and it's bring-in' the cat-tle o - ver,— Now

lis - ten while I tell to you how I be-came a dro - ver,— I

want - ed stock for Queens-land— and from Kemp - sey I did wan - der,— And I

bought a thou - sand cat-tle there — and be - came an o - ver - land - er.

Chorus

Pass the bot - tle round,— boys,— Don't you leave it stand there,—

For to-night we'll drink the health— of ev-er-y o - ver - land - er.

1. Now there's a trade you all know well and
    it's bringing the cattle over,
   Now listen while I tell to you how I
    became a drover.
   I wanted stock for Queensland, and from
    Kempsey I did wander
   And I bought a thousand cattle there and
    became an overlander.

   CHORUS
   Pass the bottle round, boys, don't you
    leave it stand there,
   For tonight we'll drink the health of
    every overlander.

2. When the cattle were counted, and the
    outfit ready to start,
   I saw the boys all mounted with their
    swags thrown on the cart.
   All kind of men I had, too, from France
    and Spain and Flanders,
   Lawyers, doctors, good and bad, in a
    mob of overlanders.

   CHORUS
   Pass the bottle round etc.

3. From the track a dam spread out, and
    the grass was green and young,
   And a squatter with a curse and shout
    told me to move along.
   I said: 'Come draw it mild, man, and
    don't you raise me dander
   For I'm a regular knowing card, and a
    Queensland overlander.'

   CHORUS
   Pass the bottle round etc.

4. We moved the cattle fifty mile and we
    camped them for a day,
   We talked about the rich folk's life, and
    our true loves far away.
   Our tucker isn't fancy, it's beef and tea
    and damper,
   But we wash it down with the Queensland
    rum and it suits the overlander.

   CHORUS
   Pass the bottle round etc.

5. Our clothes are getting dirtier, and our
    throats are choked with dust,
   So we set our tired horses free and in the
    dogs we trust.
   We gaze into the shimmering haze and
    dream of places grander,
   But come what may, we know we'll stay,
    with the Queensland overlanders.

   CHORUS
   Pass the bottle round etc.

6. Now I would scorn to steal a shirt, as
    all my mates would say,
   But if we pass a township upon a washing
    day,
   Those dirty brats of kids will shout, and
    quickly raise me dander,
   Saying: 'Mother dear, take in the clothes,
    here comes an overlander.'

   CHORUS
   Pass the bottle round etc.

7. In town we dress ourselves all up and we
    go to see a play
   And we never think of being hard up, or
    how to spend the day.
   We steer up to them pretty girls, who
    dress themselves in grandeur
   And while they spend our cheques they
    swear they love the overlanders.

   CHORUS
   Pass the bottle round etc.

Bibliography

SOURCES AND REFERENCES

In addition to the documentary materials listed hereunder, this work was based on information generously provided by a great many people concerning their first hand experiences of droving and overlanding. Those people are named in the Acknowledgements. Records of communications with them are held by the author.

Principal documentary references were:

Alexander, G. & Williams, O.B. (eds.) — *Pastoral Industries of Australia*. Sydney, Sydney University Press.

Barker, H.M. — *Droving Days*. Melbourne, Pitman, 1966.

Bennett, M.M. — *Christison of Lammermoor*. London, Alston Rivers, 1927.

Blainey, Geoffrey — *A Land Half Won*. Adelaide, Macmillan, 1980.m

Bolton, G.C. — *Alexander Forrest*. Melbourne, Melbourne University Press, 1958.

Brodribb, W.A. — *Recollections of an Australian Squatter 1835-1883*. Sydney, John Ferguson, 1978 (Facsimile Reprint)

Broughton, G.W. — *Turn Again Home*. Melbourne, Jacaranda Press, 1965.

Buchanan, Gordon — *Packhorse and Waterhole*. Sydney, Angus & Robertson, 1933.

Carter, Jeff. — *In The Tracks of the Cattle*. Sydney, Angus & Robertson, 1968.

Costello, Michael M.J. — *Life of John Costello*, Sydney, Dymocks, 1930.

Cotton, A.J. — *With The Big Herds in Australia*. Brisbane, Watson Ferguson, 1933.

Daly, Harriet W. — *Digging Squatting and Pioneering Life*. London, Sampson Low, Marston, Searle & Rivington, 1887.

Donovan, Peter Francis — *A Land Full of Possibilities*. St. Lucia, University of Queensland Press, 1981.

Duncan, Ross — *The Northern Territory Pastoral Industry 1863-1910*. Carlton (Victoria), Melbourne University Press, 1967.

Durack, Mary — *Kings in Grass Castles*. London, Constable, 1959.

Dutton, Geoffrey — *The Hero as Murderer*. Sydney, Collins, 1967.

Ford, Margaret — *Beyond the Furthest Fences*. London, Hodder & Stoughton, 1966.

Forrest, Peter and Egan, Ted — *The Overlanders*. An audio tape, Alice Springs, 1982.

Fysh, Hudson — *Taming the North*. Sydney, Angus & Robertson, 1933.

Giles, Alfred — *The First Pastoral Settlement in the N.T.* A5837, South Australian Archives, Adelaide.

Groom, Arthur — *I Saw A Strange Land*. Sydney, Angus & Robertson, 1950.

Gunn, Mrs Aeneas — *We of the Never-Never*. Richmond, Vic. Hutchinson of Australia, 1977.

Haldane, A.R.B. — *Drove Roads of Scotland*. Edinburgh, Nelson, 1952.

Harney, W.E. (Bill) — *Grief, Gaiety, and the Aborigines*. London, Hale. 1961.

Hardy, Bobby — *West of the Darling*. Milton, Qld., Jacaranda, 1969.

Harris, Douglas — *Drovers of the Outback*. Fitzroy, Vic., Globe, 1983.

Idriess, Ion L. — *The Cattle King*. Sydney, Angus & Robertson 1936.

ardine	*Narrative of the Overland Expedition of the Messrs. Jardine from Rockhampton to Cape York Northern Queensland compiled from the Journals of the brothers and edited by Frederick J. Byerley.* Brisbane, Buxton, 1867.
Kerr, Margaret	*The Overlanders.* By Margaret & Colin Kerr. Adelaide, Rigby, 1978.
Lewis, John	*Fought and Won.* Adelaide, Thomas, 1922.
Linklater, William	*Gather no Moss.* Melbourne, Macmillan of Aust., 1968.
Linklater, H.T.	*Echoes of the Elsey Saga.* Norton, N.S.W. the author, 1980.
Madigan, C.T.	*Central Australia.* Melbourne, Oxford University Press, 1944.
Makin, Jock	*The Big Run.* Adelaide, Rigby, 1970.
McCarthy, P.H.	*Starlight — The Man and the Myth.* Melbourne Hawthorn Press 1972.
McIver, George	*A Drover's Odyssey.* Sydney, Angus & Robertson, 1933.
McKnight, Tom	*The Long Paddock.* Armidale, N.S.W., University of New England, 1977.
Morton, E.	*Nanna's Memoirs.* Adelaide, Lutheran Publishing House, 1976.
Neal, S.	*An Important Place: Borrooloola 1881-1923* B.A. (Hons) Thesis, Dept. of History, Australian National University, 1977.
Nesdale, Ira	*The Little Missus Mrs. Aeneas Gunn.* Blackwater (S.A.) Lynton Publications, 1977.
Northern Territory	*Northern Territory Stock Routes. Northern Territory Animal Industry Branch, Extension Article No. 8.*
Perry, Harry	*Pioneering. The Life of the Hon. R.M. Collins, M.L.C.* Brisbane, Watson Ferguson, 1923.
Porter, J.A.	*Roll the Summers Back.* Brisbane, Jacaranda, 1961.
Powell, Alan	*Far Country.* Carlton (Vic.), Melbourne University Press, 1981.
Ratcliffe, Francis	*Flying Fox and Drifting Sand.* Sydney, Angus & Robertson, 1963.
Rose, A.L.	*Early N.T. Droving Epics.* In Australian Veterinary Journal, Vol. 40, March 1964 pp. 73-78.
Searcy, Alfred	*In Northern Seas.* Adelaide, Thomas, 1905.
Searcy, Alfred	*In Australian Tropics.* London, Robertson, 1907.
Sowden, William J.	*The Northern Territory As It Is.* Adelaide, Thomas, 1882.
Spencer, W. Baldwin	*in* Northern Administrator's Report, 1913.
Taylor, Peter	*An End To Silence.* Sydney, Methuen of Australia, 1980.
Teece, Cecil William	*Voice of the Wilderness.* (by C.W. Teece & Glenville Pike). Rockhampton, C.W. Teece, 1978.
Thonemann, H.E.	*Tell the White Man.* Sydney, Collins, 1949.
Willey, Keith	*Boss Drover.* Adelaide, Rigby, 1971.
Willey, Keith	*Ghosts of the Big Country.* Adelaide, Rigby, 1975.
Willey, Keith	*Tales of the Big Country.* Adelaide, Rigby, 1977.
Willey, Keith	*The Drovers.* Melbourne, Macmillan, 1982.
Winter-Irving, W.A.	*Further Out.* Melbourne, Nelson, 1975.
Wright, Judith	*Generations of Men.* Melbourne, Oxford University Press, 1959.

Guitar Chords

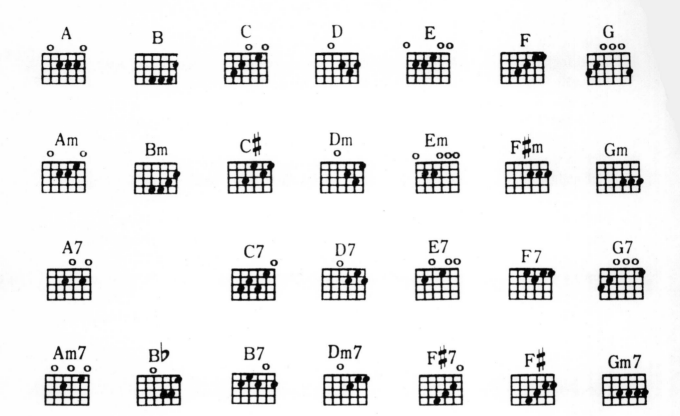